'Deeply moving and poignant, it   ᴊu in emotionally –
you don't know whether to laugh or cry, but it is impossible
to be indifferent'

Imran Ahmad, author, *Unimagined*

'A young Muslim woman in the 21st century – this book
shows you how bright, sharp, patient, funny and creative you
have to be. If I were a man I would marry her now'

Yasmin Alibhai-Brown, writer, broadcaster, columnist,
The Independent; Evening Standard

'We don't identify Christianity or Judaism completely by their
fundamentalists. This is a book that helps us to free the
Muslim community from the stupid prejudices and ignorant
labels currently waved around. In her funny and insightful
book, Nasreen Akhtar takes us into the heart
and mind of a Muslim woman who wants to get married, and
who, on the way, discovers the beautiful spirituality of her
religion. No fanatics. No prejudices. Lots of laughs and some
tears'

Joy Manné, editor, *The Healing Breath*

v

About the author

Nasreen Akhtar holds a postgraduate degree in Linguistics from Goldsmiths' College, University of London. She is a freelance copywriter and proprietor of the publishing imprint *greenbirds*. She was born in 1974 and came to the UK with her Pakistani parents at the age of four.

This is her first book.

NASREEN AKHTAR

Catch a Fish from the Sea

(Using the Internet)

First published in 2008 by greenbirds
ISBN-13: 978-0-9555214-1-6

Printed and bound in Great Britain by Mackays of Chatham, CPI Group, UK

Henri Nouw... quote, from *Out of Solitude* ... Nouwen... 2004. Used
with pe... mission ... ..., Notre Dame
– Indiana ... ... .com

Definition of ... the word 'nice' ... ... up Publishers L... 2003 and is
reprod... ...ed by permission of HarperCollins Publish... Ltd.

Definitions of ... ...rds 'soul' and 'mate' are reproduced from ...ollins Gem
English Dic... ... ... permission of HarperCollins P... shers Ltd
© HarperCollins Publishers Ltd 19...

greenbirds' p... ...cy is to use papers that are natural, re...able products made
from wood grown in sustainable forests. The manufacturing process is
expected to conform to the environmental regulations of the country of
origin.

greenbirds is an imprint of Greenbirds Ltd
Knowledge Dock Business Centre
University of East London, 4 University Way
London E16 2RD, UK
www.greenbirds.co.uk

This is for the One who created me, will cause me to die, and will raise me up again from dust and bones.

'If a man could pass through Paradise in a dream,
and have a flower presented to him as a pledge
that his soul had really been there, and if he found
that flower in his hand when he awake –
Aye, what then?'

Samuel Taylor Coleridge (1772–1834)

Contents

Foreword

S he came into my life one day, the authoress of this funny, poignant, truthful tale. Something about her unnerved yet intrigued me. She sat down on our red sofa, smiled easily, talked compellingly, made me believe she had been sent to save the world, and me from administrative hell. A dozen over-qualified men and women applied for a voluntary post to help set up a new charity organisation. This candidate wore a black scarf which framed her open face without a trace of make-up but beaming like a full moon; a light from within. I have long argued against female cover-ups but that proved to be no barrier. I liked her and felt she had depths yet to be mined. She accepted my offer with such joy; she must have liked me too.

In the first weeks we adapted to each other. She would drive over and ring the bell exactly on time. She was strict too, unrelenting on rules and conditions of her own making. No, she wouldn't eat or drink anything (ever) and was determined to be formal. The relaxed woman I had hired seemed to be disappearing before my eyes. The more I tried to break this down, the more like a regimented creature she behaved. But as time went on she started relaxing, taking off her scarf (when there were no men around) to let her beautiful hair cascade and I thought how irresistible she was; intelligent, feisty, lovely, instinctively feminist yet feminine, dissolving people with her voice and impeccable manners …

Bank managers, lawyers, bureaucrats all people I find impossible melted with her charm assaults. And then she told me about this book, this quest, the journey she was on that never had an end. How can it be? That such an Asian Muslim woman, should find herself a Bridget Jones only with better wit and without the booze, cigarettes or any bad habits, only bad luck?

Read the book and that question becomes more insistent and you begin to hear in this voice, the echo of emptiness filling these isles. How many other such women are out there, searching for soul mates, not Sharrukh Khans, just good, interesting, lively, responsible Asian Muslim men who can treat their women as equals and as creatures in need of romance, love, and sensual, as well as intellectual, pleasures? The trouble with Asian men is most haven't grown and moved as fast and far as their sisters, wives, even their mothers. The situations in this book will make you laugh and cry; men who never have cash on them; some macho jerks whose attitudes I thought had been buried in old graves containing that species of expired masculinity. The ugly ones feel entitled to beautiful and educated women; the stupid think they are owed geishas (with a few honourable and desirable exceptions of course).

So the journey goes on for this delightful young woman. Someone is there who will find and love her I know. But I hope not too soon so she can write a sequel and stay with me a little longer.

Yasmin Alibhai-Brown
February 2007

Author's Personal Note

L ife is an amazing thing: a blessing, test, gift, teacher, mentor, friend, enemy, emperor, gladiator, passing phase ... a mirage. Most of us seek the meaning of life during our short existence. This search will encompass a myriad of delights. One of these delights is finding someone who will journey with you through the splendour of this amazing thing we call life.

This book is about one woman's search. A search of hope that one day a heart, by Divine Will, would come to honour her with love and mercy contained therein. It is a true story. It is my story.

This book has been the result of much heartache and pain, laughter and tears, disappointment and fears, dark days, darker nights, spells of sunshine, roller coasters and a whole host of other emotions that I cannot even begin to describe; some I dare not imagine.

This book is for all those who have ever experienced that endless maze of trying to find a hand to hold and, despite their despondency, still carry in their hearts that stubborn hope that someday, someway, they will find that one person ...

So here's to dreams; those realised, those yet to conquer, and those that will never come to be.

Nasreen Akhtar
London 2007

Prologue

This is the story of an ordinary girl who searched high and low for an extraordinary guy. But the problem she found was that extraordinary guys want extraordinary girls. So you can see my predicament already.

I am a thirty*something* female, British Asian and of Pakistani origin. The Pakistani/South Asian/female aspect was set right from my conception. The British came in many years later, at the very cute age of six, when I was naturalised a citizen of Great Britain and, of course, I wasn't always thirty*something*.

I was twenty-six years of age when I first entertained the idea of going out into the big, bad world to try to find someone with whom I could settle down and have many babies. Up until then, whenever the word 'marriage' was mentioned, it would set off an unknown chemical reaction devouring my whole body like a drop of ink consuming a glass of clear water.

This reaction has been a great friend of mine ever since I can remember. As a child, once I had passed that adolescent age when *boys* repulsed me, I promised myself that I would never (ever) get married. The Western women on TV were single and free and I wanted that too. What was marriage if nothing but totally ruining your life? I saw misery around me and I was going to make sure that that didn't happen to me. Then the pestiferous teenage years kicked in. Romance and love familiarised themselves with me and so things began to change.

Our neighbours, an elderly English couple, totally wonderful people, asked me once, '*So are you going to have an arranged marriage?*' An absolutely cringe-inducing question, despised by almost every British Asian female; a most hated question on a par with the equally discomforting, '*Why aren't you married yet?*' or the even more suffocating, '*When are you getting married then?*'

'Never,' I told them.

I didn't even want to think about marriage, let alone to someone I didn't know. The idea of having no control over your life; that someone else dictated who you married and who you didn't made me uneasy. So I have had a hate-hate relationship with the words '*arranged* marriage' since forever. Every time that horrid question was asked, I remember turning into the Incredible Hulk. The mere thought of the *arranged* marriage mortified me.

It conjured up all sorts of unwanted and unthinkable images. Images that I would make sure wouldn't become my reality. This fact everyone knew. I knew, my family knew and even the worm in the garden knew. And so they all left me to it (especially the worm in the garden).

By the age of twenty-six, after officially having reached the 'Best Before Date' in the Pakistani Marriage Supermarket, my poor father decided that it was time he took matters into his own hands and defy the sanctions I had imposed. Quite dutifully, he lived up to his paternal role and tried to find his daughter a 'suitable match'. Religiously, every Saturday, he would buy the UK *Urdu Daily*, turn to the exclusive matrimonial section which was a special feature catering for desperate fathers trying to get rid of their daughters, and meticulously he would find the:

'Hum apne beteh, 29, handsome, computer analyst, keh liey achey gharaney ka rishta dhoond rahey hain. Larkhi must be maximum age 26, educated and pretty. Parental involvement necessary.'

Loosely translated that means:

'We are looking for a good match from a respectable household, for our son, 29, handsome, computer analyst. Girl must be 26 max.'

… The rest is self-explanatory I guess. Or is it? …

Don't these adverts, especially the ones placed by parents, seem to have a language of their own? Literary forensics of the aforementioned advert reveals an interesting picture. What it actually says is something along of the lines of:

'Looking for submissive virgin whose parents are not *divorced* (oh the shame of that horrid word).

Our son, quite possibly nearer to 40, is 'in computers' and lives at home. For the sake of syntax, let's randomly throw in a word … this will do … 'handsome'. He is handsome.

The girl must be less than sell by date of 26 so that the community doesn't wonder why our daughter-in-law wasn't married at a more acceptable age. After all, there obviously has got to be something wrong in her biological programming if she has passed the age of 25 and remains unmarried. Even 26 is pushing it slightly, but it is closer to 25 than 27. Twenty-seven obviously says, *'Hey look at me, I am probably infertile,'* or worse still it shouts out, *'Hey world look at me, I have been delaying the whole marriage thing all this time because I have a boyfriend but really I have been pulling the wool over my parents eyes telling them I wanted a career first.'*

Did we mention that she must be stunningly breathtakingly gorgeous and a brain surgeon at the same time? Well she must because we want Saeeda Apa to be jealous.

Parental involvement is necessary so that we can establish whether you would be at the same level as us and whether our caste will allow you to sit on the sofa with us, or on the floor; while we sit on the sofa – of course.'

For those who think that the above is an exaggeration, I can assure you that there is more truth in what I have said than you can possibly know. What is perhaps worse is that not much has changed in the last few decades or so.

When my family was looking for that 'suitable match' for my sisters, the politics were exactly the same. I remember those days when my poor old father would sift through the adverts in the same manner that he did when it came to me.

We had many *our young son* matches for my sisters. 'Young men' who were never quite the age that their adverts said they were. Back then, parents were notorious for fabricating the truth when it came to age.

'Why is that?' I once asked.

'Because it is not good to be unmarried, especially if you have many years behind you,' my mother would say.

Clearly, this stigma of being *advanced in years yet behind the ranks of the married* was an almost shameful phenomenon. But on the plus side it was a comfort to know that this social taboo also touched the male sector of Pakistani society and wasn't confined to just the womenfolk.

So, every time there was a sighting of a potential *rishta* [candidate for marriage], initial contact, in the form of a letter had to be sent to the P.O. Box c/o the newspaper. They would pass the mail on and interested parties would then exercise their prerogative of whether they wanted to reply and whether a subsequent meeting would take place. Relatively harmless, yes, unless of course you came from a single-parent family, in which case there were numerous hurdles along the way; the first being that all important and ever so decisive phone call.

'When the authoritative fathers rang, they would want to speak to my dad so I would hand over the phone. However, if it was the boy's mother, she would want to speak to the girl's mother and that is when a *situation* would arise,' Labiba once told me. 'I would have to explain to the *Aunties* the reason why they couldn't speak to my mother and then have to put up with the awkwardness that would fill the air because of which they would scurry to get off the phone.'

Growing up with just the one parent had repercussions when it came to thriving in some sort of social circle. A single father would hardly spread the word that his daughter of *marryable age* needed a suitable suitor. Even if he wanted to, how would he do it? Who would he approach? Culturally, it was the mother's role to socialise with the right people in the hope that someone somewhere would be interested in her daughter; hence the 'arrangement' of the *arranged marriage*.

Of course, these days there are various degrees of '*arranged marriage*'. You can easily produce a whole survey scale of 1–5; 1 being the, '*Extremely and so very arranged marriage that it is forced*' to the, '*My mum knew someone who knew someone*' arranged marriage to the, '*We got to talk to each other on the phone*' arranged marriage to the, '*Going out with him for months or even years and then telling my parents that if they didn't marry me to him then I would run away*' arranged marriage, and 5 being the, '*I arranged the caterers, the flowers, the photographer, the transport and my lehnga* [bridal dress]' arranged marriage. But back then, it was a different story altogether.

The newspaper route (which probably sits somewhere between 1 and 2 on the scale above) was a last resort and so, by some unofficial logic, anybody who went down this road to find a marriage prospect was some kind of reject; a social outcast. This stigma was magnified further if the mother was a single parent searching for a suitable match for her children. If a widow, then that was acceptable; anything otherwise was shunned horrendously.

But even in situations where both mother and father were very much together, sometimes parents would still find themselves at a lost end when it came to arranging their children's marriages. The fact was neither of my parents knew anyone nor were part of the *community* where introductions were possible; so the newspaper route was the final and only resort they could explore.

Brace yourselves now please. I am about to tell you about my first and last ever experience via the newspaper matrimonials. (Now may be a good time to go get yourself a cup of tea.)

One: Some People Are Coming to See You

My sister is a terrible communicator. When she found out that she was *with child* she sat in my room for a good twenty minutes, suddenly taking an interest in me and my life. Out of the sheer frustration of knowing that she wanted to tell me something, even knowing what she wanted to tell me, yet her not getting to the point, I asked, '*You're expecting, aren't you?*' I was careful not to say the word 'pregnant' for fear that she may disappear into thin air from the shame of it all even though she was married.

Similarly, on that particular Thursday afternoon, she had been hovering around me for nearly an hour trying to be normal, not realising that she knew that I knew that she wanted to talk to me about something, and that I knew that she didn't know that I knew what it was regarding. *A moment please as I just go over the last sentence to make sure that it does make sense.*

I should tell you more about my sister. Even though she looks like me (we are often mistaken for twins) and sounds like me, she is actually nothing like me, because she is, in fact, not me. I am more open in my approach to life, whereas for her there were certain things you just didn't entertain, let alone vocalise.

Boys, periods and that other thing a man and a woman do, and then nine months later they have a little human being, we never talked about any of that stuff. In my family almost everything was taboo and the subject of marriage was like dynamite. I don't think there has been any sexual activity in any corner of this house for a few decades. Even the mice under the floorboards have probably signed the 'Official *Sexuals* Act', prohibiting them from fulfilling their carnal desires.

So, you can imagine what my sister must have gone through. I don't know what was worse for her – having to tell me that some *people* were coming to 'view me' for their son or the fact that if I passed the viewing, I might be having 'sexual relations' (thanks to Bill Clinton for enriching the English vocabulary) with a man.

Like bee to nectar, my sister hovered around me that afternoon trying to send me a barrage of telepathic messages. When that didn't work, she eventually gathered the courage,

'… Make sure you are in on Saturday,' she said, attempting to leave the room.

'Excuse me?!? … Where do you think you are going?' I exclaimed, sprinting across the room faster than any action hero could have done.

'Some people are coming to see you,' she said, all flustered, before making a quick exit. If there was ever a world record for one, she had just broken it.

The next few days felt as if my family was preparing for a celebration. It was manic and unbelievable and I hated every minute. Anyone would think that it was my wedding day. My dad acted as if these people were my new in-laws and would carry me away on an elephant, like in a Bollywood movie. If it had been up to him, he would have changed the wallpaper in all the rooms and had new carpet laid down; but alas, there was only one day left until the *guests* came, and so varnishing the stairs and painting the downstairs bathroom was about all that he could manage.

'But Dad, they are not going to be inspecting the bathroom, just your daughter,' I felt like saying to him, before it suddenly dawned upon me that maybe the whole idea was to display me in the bathroom.

They were only coming for tea, but it was like an Indian restaurant in my house with menus being discussed ardently. If I hadn't stepped in, they would've started interviewing for waiting staff. Amidst all the *excitement* I remained unaffected. I hadn't even bothered to ask who this guy was, but it was mentioned to me in passing (as if I cared) that he had some business in America (or *'Amreeka'* if you really want to pronounce it correctly) and was coming over to the UK for two weeks in search of a bride. This probably meant that he was illegal and waiting for his Green Card.

On the day of my potential in-laws' arrival, my sister began to get slightly worried that I wasn't getting ready. '*Getting ready*' in Pakistani terms means dressed and made up as if going for a magazine cover photo shoot. I refused to 'get ready.' I wasn't a doll or even an object that they were coming to 'inspect' to see if they found me attractive.

I had been told that this wasn't a *forced* marriage and that I wasn't obligated to say *yes*. Of course I had the right to choose;

if I liked him I had to say and they would take things further. If not, then that was it. This was only an introduction.

Introduction …?? Let's, for one unthinkable split stroke of a second, assume that I did 'like' this guy based solely on looks, what would happen?

'Well, Dad would talk with his parents and they would discuss arrangements.'

'And where would I live?'

'You would have to move.'

'What if I didn't want to move?'

'But you would have to.'

'And these arrangements, what would they be?'

'You know, stuff.'

'What sort of stuff?'

'Just stuff.'

'Well what if I don't get on with him?'

'You learn to overcome it.'

'What if I don't learn to overcome it?'

'You will. That is the way it is.'

'Well I don't want this.'

'It's just scary, but it's not that bad. We had to go through it.'

'If you want a medal, I don't have one to give you. And it is bad and I am not going to put up with it.'

'Look, you have to get married one day.'

'So?'

'So, nothing, what other way is there?'

'There must be other ways, and I tell you, it's got to be better than this one.'

'Well we can talk another time. Let's get this over and done with.'

'We can get this over and done with right now. Why don't you give me their phone number and I will tell them to ***%^$&'

Unfortunately I wasn't given the chance to articulate my feelings because soon after, the doorbell rang. And it rang. And it rang. And it just kept ringing. Just my luck that no one was in; my mother had gone to the shops, my father was at the *masjid* [mosque] and my sisters went home (I suspect to put on their jewellery). If you are South Asian, you will understand. If you are not South Asian, you may want to know that some women from our community like to take advantage of such occasions and display their collection of 22-carat Asian-gold earrings, necklaces, bangles and bracelets. So I was the only one left to open the door to our *guests*, who were of course probably expecting me to be wearing lots of gold jewellery too.

I prayed so much that they would just knock a few times and then leave quietly but I soon discovered that prayers, although listened to, aren't always answered that quickly and sometimes you have to take a ticket and wait in the queue. It was as if they somehow knew that they were not welcome but felt the need to chronically **** me off with their persistent bell ringing. (I realise that the publisher has probably blotted out the foul language using a few stars.)

I wanted to leave them standing there, but their endless ringing of the doorbell was driving me so crazy that I had to force myself to open the door. I was dressed in my *lazing around the house attire*, with which my potential mother-in-law was not pleased. I could tell her disapproval from the unimpressed look she shot at me as I let them in. After the forced, pleasant, *'Hello, hello, how are you?'* coupled with the silent, *'Come in and I hope you choke on the food and please take your son with you,'* I let Auntie in, followed by Uncle. Naturally, I mean who heard of a Pakistani family where the lady did not wear the *shalwar?*[1]

Behind them was a horrid looking 'young man' who was eyeing me up so much that I wanted to pull his eyes out and gently place them in his shirt pocket. I showed them into the lounge before proceeding to send out smoke signals as a desolate plea for someone to come and save my soul.

The eagles had landed firmly and were left sitting alone for a good fifteen minutes before the doorbell rang once more. I was so traumatised by the unfolding events that I refused to go downstairs and open the door again. It was my father at the door. He had forgotten his key. In the end I think it was the guy who got up to open the door for him. I didn't like the look of him already, trying to 'get in there' with his 'father-in-law.' I mean, who asked him to open the door in the first place? If that was some feeble chivalrous attempt to impress me, it wasn't going to work. I didn't care how gracefully a man could open the front door to my house. I did not want an *arranged* marriage / *introduction* or whatever they wanted to call it and no one could make me.

---

1 Traditional Pakistani trousers

The longer they sat in my house the more I cried. This was awful. This was probably worse than awful. Was this what I would have to go through every time people came to my house to take me off my father's hands? This was not a good feeling. I cried and waited for 'movement' in the house, ready with my archery set, willing to employ *any means necessary* to fight off the aggressors who sought to take away my fundamental civil and human rights by removing me from my bedroom and taking me downstairs; to the lounge.

An hour went by and my sister came upstairs. After catapulting all known shoes in the house at her, I politely let it be known that I would not be gracing everyone with my presence.

'Are you crazy? You can't stay here the whole time!' she said.

'No, but I think that you are if you think that I am going to go downstairs.'

Never having been a rebel teenager, I felt the need to make up for lost time on that particular day, and it felt good to be able to take the, *I am not going to clean my room and you can't make me* stance on things.

'Look, I understand what you are going through and I don't blame you. But it will look bad if you don't come down,' she said.

I didn't care though so I sent her back empty handed. Ten minutes later, she returned.

'Just tell them that they have already seen me as I was the one who opened the door,' I tried to barter.

'We already did, and the mother turned around and said, *What kind of people are you? How were we supposed to know that that was the girl?'*

'Well, what do they want to do; observe me under a microscope?' I asked.

Minutes later she came upstairs again, 'Look, his mother is getting annoyed, you'd better come down right now,' she said angrily.

I knew she was serious when my suggestion that she take down my passport and show them my photo didn't work. Reluctantly, I headed towards the door ready to go down before I was stopped. Apparently the clothes I was wearing were *unsuitable.*

The truth was that I didn't have any 'suitable' clothes. The fact that I barely possessed Asian clothes meant that the Western clothing that I did have was naturally unsuitable. Any respectable mother would obviously frown at my choice of garments. Even though they were loose, modest items of clothing, somehow my sister seemed to think that it reflected badly on them. What would people think? What would the boy's mother say to her friends, *'We went to see a girl, and she was not even wearing shalwar kameez!'* [Pakistani clothing]

I was tired of arguing and retaliating. I needed to get this over and done with. The quicker I conformed, the quicker they would be out of my house; that sounded good ... very good in fact. Having made my sister solemnly promise that I would only be in that room for as long as necessary, I agreed for her to dress me up like a Christmas tree. This would also

give me a ticket out of there; I couldn't stay long as I was
going out to a party!

'Wear some make-up and do your hair,' she said as I
headed towards the staircase.

'Don't push it now,' I responded and off I went to the
gallows.

I went downstairs to find my father sitting there in the room
and so ... I walked back out again. I just couldn't go in. I had
never felt so embarrassed in all my life. It was one thing to
draw blood and dip my bleeding arm into the shark pool but
to do it in my father's presence? No, I couldn't. I just couldn't.
He understood and said that it was best that he leave. Thank
God for that!

With a push and a shove, I found myself sitting with the
guests, opposite his parents and parallel to 'him'. I was so glad
that he was sitting on the chair otherwise I would've had to
hire architects to build a wall on our sofa (which does not
have home-made floral settee covers, may I just add).

I looked on as my sisters tried to justify why I was late
coming down to join everyone. The excuse was as suspicious
as it sounded. His mother sat there looking at me, wondering
why I was wearing fancy clothes and shoes yet my face was
bare, make-up less and my hair looking as if I had just been
dragged through a bush backwards. Biting my tongue trying to
hold in an array of emotions that were intent on jumping out
and performing the hula, I sat there, unable to look at his
mother or his father. I had decided that he wasn't even worth
looking at, and so I carried on ignoring his existence.

His parents attempted to exchange pleasantries, before moving on to 'interview' me as I sat there on the *Mastermind* chair. His mother started asking me questions; questions that were deliberately designed to confuse me. Questions like, *'What is your name, Nasreen?'*

'With all due respect, why ask me a question to which you already know the answer?' I felt like saying. But envisaging the aftermath, I thought it best to exercise my prerogative of silence. Besides, every time I tried to respond, nothing would come out; and so all of a sudden, the carpet seemed like the most interesting thing in the world.

His mother continued with the interrogation whilst I wrestled with the next question, 'How old are you?' At that moment in time, to be honest, perhaps even I didn't know my name, or my age. All I knew was that there was a guy on my left, gawping at me as if he had never seen a woman before and, worse still, he was sitting there all smug, thinking that he was going to marry me!

'In your dreams,' I thought, as I walked out of the room.

Yes that is right, I asked to be excused and I left. It was as simple as that.

I didn't even bother with the follow-up after they had left. I was just so glad that they were gone. It was such a horrific experience for me and I couldn't care less. I had expected that my father would send out a feedback questionnaire but he didn't. I think the fact that I went on a hunger strike was a strong indication that I was not impressed by the newspaper route. Days later when I did start eating again (and who can resist chicken biryani unless you are a vegetarian), my sister took that as the green light to approach me for comment, asking me and I quote, '*So what did you think then?*'

I looked at her, held her gaze for a few seconds and then walked away. We never spoke about this again. It was obvious to me and it soon became obvious to them all, that whereas my sisters had been the *obedient daughters*, I would be the opposite. Even though my parents were relieved that I had managed to get through my teenage years without being a rebel to society and culture and not disgracing their good names (too much), it seemed as if I had been investing all that energy over the years and would channel it into resisting the smooth transition to marriage. They were right of course.

For me, at that point, 'marriage' was a ghastly word. It was scary enough without having to deal with the prospect of being lumbered with a stranger. I did not want to get married their way or on their terms. Why should I? What about me? It was just something that was an obligation to my family; God would not be happy until my parents fulfilled their parental duties and married me off. Exactly what marriage was, I did not know. All I knew was that I didn't like the ideology that was attributed to it by the Pakistani culture, or indeed the wider South Asian culture to which belonged the Pakistani subset.

As Asians from the Indian subcontinent, I think it is generally understood that marriage has nothing to do with love. It is as if there is no room for 'love' in a marriage and that the two components are unrelated. Growing up in the

UK, in a predominantly Asian neighbourhood, when someone did get married, the first question that would be asked was if so and so had a *love* marriage or an *arranged* marriage. Should the response be the former, then that was high scandal. If it was the latter, however, then the girl was obviously 'good', 'respectable', and 'decent'.

Perhaps that is why I avoided the marriage issue. I didn't want nosey neighbours putting me in their 'categories' and I certainly did not want to be joined to *man with moustache*. If that wasn't bad enough, I couldn't picture myself amongst fancy Asian clothes, jewellery, cars and the nightmare of the wedding *movie*. Did I want all that? No. And I didn't want what came after. Nor did I want what came before.

From what I knew of tradition; the boy's family visited the girl's family and the girl brought in the tea and biscuits. If the boy's family found her attractive then things would progress. They would come a second time and finalise the wedding. It didn't matter if the personalities did not mix, what was important was that the families were wealthy, the girl could cook and clean, look after his parents, run the house, raise the children, please her husband and most of all look good. It was better that she didn't have a brain because that way she would be able to think for herself and this was not a desired trait.

So, if this is what marriage was, and I was sure that I didn't want it, then why was I even entertaining the idea? I had fast approached twenty-seven years of age, and started to feel past my *sell by* date. I was going through a phase where I was so convinced that my insides would somehow curl up and disintegrate if I didn't have a baby there and then. But I didn't want all this 'traditional' business. I wanted a shining knight who would come on his white horse …

Years later, I found myself still waiting. He obviously needed a satellite navigation system (designed for horses of course). Although I have just made a highly valid observation, that is not the point though. The point is that I needed to find my man, my way, by myself. I couldn't let them humiliate me through the disgraceful newspaper route or any sort of parental involvement.

So I turned to the World Wide Web.

Two: Make Way, Make Way; Coming Through

The Internet. What a marvellous invention! Sometimes I wonder how we as human beings ever survived without it. These days you can do almost everything on the net. You can pay bills, research essays, run a business, look for a job, even look for a partner. And that is exactly what I decided to do.

Ironically, the *Urdu Daily* did prove its worth. I must quickly redeem myself by telling you that I was peeling potatoes when one fell to the floor. As I picked it up and placed it on the newspaper sheet laid out on the kitchen worktop, I noticed a website address. As if by fate, a whole new world opened up for me just there and then. It was all there in black and white print; an outside world (albeit virtual) did exist and I was about to dive into it.

There was one small problem though: I could not use computers. I hated them. A doctoral thesis I could write with my eyes closed, but when it came to computers, I was illiterate. However, images of being married to *man with moustache* whizzed in my mind and I knew that I had to face my I.T. phobia or be doomed forever. I chose the former. And so with a wing and a prayer, I typed in the words 'Muslim Matrimonials' and let the search engines do their work.

Man of my dreams, I was coming to get you.

Three: First Steps

W hen I first started looking, I took many things for
granted and thought it would be *easy peasy lemon squeezy*.
I would throw a few words together to create my *profile*, post it
on a website, someone would reply and hey presto – I would
be married. Then I came to discover bitter reality. I thought
that within a few weeks Prince Charming would arrive and
that would be it. I can safely confirm that that did not happen.

The first guy I ever spoke with lived millions and millions
of miles away. As soon as I read 'I am based in Aberdeen' in
his first email, my mind went into overdrive. Which flights
would I need to catch to come visit my folks? Would he wear
a kilt in his spare time? Would he make me eat haggis? (Halal[2]
naturally.)

You must excuse me, but as my photographer friend
Allison Pereira astutely observes:

'On the whole, women are married and pregnant well
before they have even exchanged words with a guy.'

So when my morning sickness subsided and I finally spoke
with Mr Aberdeen, he politely requested that I tell him
something about myself. Now I have tremendous difficulty
talking about myself, so after a slight tug of war, he started to

---

2 That which is lawful for Muslims; in this context, it refers to meat which
is slaughtered according to Islamic guidelines.

divulge about a great love in his life: bodybuilding. I think he thought that I would be rather impressed with that but I was sorry to disappoint. I cannot think of a greater turn-off. Besides, baby oil was meant for babies.

We talked for a while and I pretended that I understood his accent when really I didn't have a clue what he was saying. I thought I had to tell him my whole life story in that first conversation, so that he could decide if he wanted to marry me, and then I would go and tell my dad. We decided to speak again, and then 'take things further', although I wasn't sure how much 'further' things were going to go. The next day, he rang me.

'Effort ats me.'

'I am sorry … Do you come with a manual?' I asked.

Needless to say, things went no further, but Mr Muscle did leave me with food for thought. '*What are you looking for in a guy?*' he had asked. It was a bizarre question at the time, and I remember saying to him, 'I don't know; a guy I guess.' … If there was a Nobel Prize for being articulate, I most certainly deserved it.

I sat down and reflected because thinking whilst standing is not as effective. What did I want? … A man, yes; but what sort of man? … This matrimonial thingy was going to be difficult; men were just men, weren't they? I was unaware that there was actually some variety to them. This was worrying. My advert – '*Everything a man could want in a woman seeks everything a woman could want in a man*' would prove to be redundant … or would it?

An eligible bachelor replied, asking if my advert was tailor-made for him … After the usual pleasantries via the matrimonial site, he asked for my email address.

'That is a smart name; I love it!' he said.

I always wanted a man who would note the more insignificant things and I liked the sound of him already. He was thirty-four years of age, and I, twenty-seven. I had visions of my sisters shaking their heads and saying, '*He is so old for you.*' Don't forget that, at that time, ultimately my marriage partner had to be to everyone else's approval and liking, where what I thought was somehow irrelevant. Subsequently, I tried not to rock the boat too much. After all they were giving me freedom of choice in marriage partner and I was grateful.

From a personal viewpoint anyway, in those days, a thirty-plus guy was unappealing. I remember discussing this one evening with my best friend. (She is called Varsha by the way and you will be hearing that name a lot as the book progresses.)

'You know what Nasreen? I think you need someone in his thirties; I would say even mid-thirties because you are quite mature,' she said.

No way! I was happy staying with men in my age range. Twenty-seven, twenty-eight, twenty-nine was as far as I was prepared to go. What I didn't realise is that there is a clause in the best friend contract which states something to the effect that, '*Best friends sometimes know more about us than we actually do or think that we do.*' And so, years later, I came to eat my words. The more I have evolved as a woman, I have discovered my own likes and dislikes and now, at the ripe young age of thirty-two, I find myself uninterested in men my age or younger than me! There is nothing more alluring than a little bit of grey, life experience, maturity … and that is what I found with Mr Slightly Older.

After our first conversation, I was left surprised by how attractive I had found him. He was so well spoken, articulate, humorous even (but obviously not as good as me). He had been at the golf club when he had rung, and joked that having been a member for a few years, he thought it was about time that he made an appearance so that they knew he existed!

He was a surgeon by profession and I was not really sure if I wanted a man who would come along and make changes to my grey matter. I liked my twisted and incomprehensible brain. Also, his privileged background and upmarket lifestyle made me nervous. For all those thinking that that doesn't matter, well perhaps it doesn't, but at that time it did, to me it did. He, a successfully established professional, living in the heart of London, would probably want an equally successful professional lady; whereas I was studying for my Masters' degree thus 'poor student' suited me appropriately. Secondly he had stated in his profile that he sought a stunning woman, so why was he wasting his time with me?

I decided that I couldn't pursue anything with this man, for to do so would just be an embarrassment. The conversation was pleasant but I had to look at the wider picture, and it wasn't looking too great. So, I went back to the drawing board.

As I browsed through the hundreds of potential son-in-law profiles for my father, I checked my mail. There in front of me was a message from him. He had sent it many hours before our conversation, so while I was talking to him, I had been unaware that he had mailed me. He spoke about how intrigued he was by my response, and how much he enjoyed my correspondence. (*This old thing?*)

After having spoken to a few guys who asked me to tell them a 'little about myself', I decided that I had better think about who I was, and what I wanted. Up until that moment, I could answer neither of those questions. So, I put together a few mundane facts about myself and sent them to him. He was impressed by them. And I was impressed that he was impressed.

He was so impressed that he sent me an attachment with that email. I opened it and at first could see nothing. I attributed that to my highly advanced I.T. skills. Upon closer inspection, it became clear that the attachment was a photo of some sort. The image was so minute it was almost drowned by white background, but after tilting to the left and then to the right, doing the hokey-cokey, turning around and zooming in, I discovered that it was a photograph of a field. Why was the guy sending me a photo of a field? What a strange thing to do?

Then I looked closely. I could fathom out a field of flowers … The word 'tulips' sprang to mind and my heart just leapt to the ground … Tulips are my most favourite flower in the (whole wide big big) world and in the details about myself, under *Likes*, I had mentioned 'Tulips in Spring'. I think that was probably the most romantic thing that had ever happened to me up until that point in my life.

Considering that he had sent me this mail, hours before I had spoken to him, I was unaware of his charm. This was both positive and negative. Positive because I am a big softie when it comes to all things romantic; and negative because it just showed me how mature and attentive he was. How would I cope with someone like that? I didn't have any experience of a real relationship so this was all too much for me.

I tried not to think about it, as I was convinced that I wouldn't be hearing from him again but he proved me wrong. We were in touch again and arranged to meet. Even though he was after a supermodel, he didn't ask for a photograph. He was happy to just meet me and I was running out of reasons not to be interested in him.

We met on a most glorious afternoon when the beautiful transition of seasons was in full swing. Autumn was beginning to work its magic on the leaves, with the sun kissing the sky with nostalgia of a romantic summer that had just slipped through its grasp. I had gone over to his office and as soon as I had walked into reception, immediately I knew that I didn't belong there. I looked around me and it felt as if I was in a five-star hotel.

When he emerged, he was a perfect gentleman, opening doors for me as we left. I like all that. I even rejected a few men on account that they had no manners. Manners feature high on my list and when a man expects a woman to open the door, it shows a lack of them. Even worse is when a man opens the door and goes first, leaving it to slam just when she gets there; husband material that is not! Looking back, it's quite funny that when I did meet potential suitors, I would look out for this. Any man who didn't open the door for me would automatically be shown a mental yellow card. My surgeon, however, was not.

We walked over to the private garden which was just outside his office, contemplating if we should go grab lunch or sit in the park and soak up the afternoon sun. We were on our way to the café when we changed plan. I know, I am terrible like that, but for what it was worth, it wasn't as if we had sat down in the eaterie and then walked out *(… How embarrassing would that be?)*.

Physically, I was not hugely attracted to him but looks are not everything, I know. I liked his personality; he was lovely. The looks thing wasn't even an issue in the end. I am a fairly domesticated woman, and at that time, I had numerous responsibilities. He made a comment about that which offended me but I kept quiet. We were two different people whose lifestyles would never find common ground and so I could not see myself a *doctor's* wife. We parted amicably. I was fully convinced that I would not hear from him again.

To my surprise, when I came home, I found another photograph in my inbox. This time it was the most breathtaking arrangement of yellow cut flowers in a most grand vase. It brought a smile to my face, for it was the second on my list of *Likes* – Fresh Cut Flowers. The euphoria was short-lived though as I had to tell him that I didn't appreciate his comment. Emails bounced back and forth, and I although I did accept his apology, our friendship, relationship, contact, or whatever the correct word would be here, had become tainted.

I don't actually know what happened between us. I think there was a point where I did ask him what he wanted to do. Either he married me or he didn't. If he didn't, then I needed to carry on with my search, and if he did, then he should hurry up and get on with it. His reply diplomatically signalled that he couldn't make a decision like that and that he wanted to be *friends*. And if something developed, it developed.

In theory that is a great approach; to naturally fall into something but, as bizarre as it may sound to some readers, had this potential match been introduced via the family I probably would have been married to this man already. That was the reality. We had met; we had spoken, so what was the delay?

I could see both sides of the argument. A person goes on a matrimonial website to find someone to marry. If people then want to go down the *'Let's get to know each other for a while, and then take it from there'* then surely that is not a matrimonial venture; then it becomes 'dating', right? It is all too much of a mind explosion I know. So you can imagine how I felt, especially since my father would count the days in angst with his stopwatch furiously doing laps by the second, wondering why it was taking me so long to find someone.

Getting back to Mr Surgeon, we lost touch after that and when we were in contact again, a few years down the line, he invited me to a masquerade ball in the most exclusive of Central London venues.

As fabulous as it sounded, my life was already a big masquerade and I couldn't handle any more.

Four: Couples

Rigorously, I carried on with the search; emailing, speaking and meeting many men, all to no avail. There was obviously something wrong with me. Everyone I knew was married and adding to the human race. And then there was me … You know that '*Inside I am dying*' syndrome? Well, I am fully versed with that. Having smug married friends doesn't help either.

When we were younger, my group of friends planned each other's lives. Who would get married first; have children first, and so on and so forth. At college, they all thought that somehow I would be first off the spinster list. I hope none of them became clairvoyants. If they did, then make sure you don't waste your money going to see them.

There is one friend of mine in particular, who, without doubt, is the founding member of what I refer to as the *Condescending Couples Network* (hereafter, CCN). Annually, without fail, she rings to inform me how she is married, and that I am not; how she is a mother, and that I am not; how she has a husband and that I do not. I must say I 'appreciate' her calls so much. The last time she rang, she asked me quite sternly whether my marital status had changed since her last *customer-care* call. Upon hearing my reply she cordially reminded me that I needed to hurry up, considering that even Shobna was going out with someone and was planning to announce her engagement in the next few weeks. Now this does not affect your life one bit, I know, but I think there is something you need to know so that you too will feel my pain.

You know how sometimes there are certain friends you just cannot picture being with anyone? Well Shobna was that certain friend of ours. We all knew that she would probably want the arranged marriage. However, at the same time there were also bets that she would be *Spinster Auntie* to all our children.

The President of the CCN let it be known that there was something severely wrong if even Shobna was walking down that path to wedded bliss, whereas I was still stuck in the singledom maze. Funnily enough, since I started writing this, Shobna has now married and is happy. I realise that sometimes these two concepts don't always sit well together, but she is married and happy. To make matters worse, she married her English boyfriend and there was absolutely no trace of the word 'arranged' in her marriage (except for the ordering of flowers and the hiring of the reception venue).

Another friend of mine from a different branch of the CCN will often spend hours telling me how good her husband is, how happy and lucky she is to have found him and how she couldn't imagine her life without him and now their son. Once in a while she will pause and reassure me, pitifully of course, that I too will 'find someone, some day'.

I think that all single girls on this planet need to start a petition outlawing the use of that phrase in our presence. Don't couples understand that we don't need their pity because we have plenty of our own?! Out of sheer frustration,

I did point this out to my do-gooder married friend recently, to which she turned around and told me that I had 'issues'.

Issues? I don't think so. Although I must admit that I am so desperate to hear the words 'I love you' that maybe I should go stand on a mountain and shout them.

Five: You Are Better Off Single!

Not only is the grass greener on the other side, but it is replete with four-leaved clovers and even a pot of gold hidden there somewhere. Single people complain that they are alone whilst the married complain that they are not. The amount of miserable married women I have come across or have heard about is astonishing. If I sat here collecting pennies for every time someone told me not to get married, then I would have a huge number of pennies.

An old school friend, who lost touch well over a decade ago, looked me up last year.

'I thought you would turn around and say to me, *Nighat, I am now married to some hunk.*'

Since I was unable to claim this, she went on to tell me that I was *better off being single.* 'Marriage ruins your life anyway,' she continued. (... Not exactly the ideal thing to say to a woman who is deliberately seeking it.)

She had had an arranged marriage but, unlike her sister who got married on the same day and also to a husband from abroad, sadly for Nighat there was no happy ending. It turned out that Nighat's husband had given her more heartache than she could have imagined and felt that she could endure.

He was a drunk and a junkie and, despite the many attempts on her part to keep the marriage together, it was a shambles. A mother of two with a third on the way, she told me of the misery in which she lived. Whilst I understand the desperation of people who think that maybe new babies are the answer to a crumbling marriage, deep down I think even they know that it is not.

Then there is the cheating man who is also a major headache. Another friend, who was married at the age of seventeen because her parents were frightened that she, like her sisters, would run away from home, was as miserable as Nighat. She too kept on having baby after baby thinking that perhaps with the arrival of the next one, he would stop straying. Forever ringing up numbers that she would find, the paranoia that surrounded her was both frightening and sad at the same time. What a life to live; constantly wondering if the woman that your husband is looking at or speaking with is also sharing a bed with him. Coincidentally, I saw her today, holding a newborn. *I hope that isn't hers*, I thought to myself. It was. He is three weeks old. He is her seventh baby. Maybe her husband *loves kids* because he knows that having them in abundance will keep her occupied with less time for her to chase him and discover his moonlighting?

Then there is the friend who married because it was a parent's last dying wish. Her father had asked his daughter to do this favour for him, as it was his duty to bring the son of his widowed sister over to this country. It must be heartbreaking to be caught up in a web like that. Now she has a daughter whom, as you would expect, she loves dearly. Both she and her husband feel trapped, but they both agree that for the sake of their little girl they must try. At least she has the sense not to produce any more children.

I sometimes wonder if these girls find themselves in these predicaments because they have no education further than secondary school level and so are forced by their parents to go abroad and marry. But I would be wrong to think that.

Another friend who recently got married gave me the very same pearls of wisdom, *'Trust me it's better to be single.'* She, a graduate and now medical student, suddenly announced a year ago that she was getting married. The parents had reluctantly accepted it, but wanted her to wait, as they thought that at twenty-two she was slightly young. She was, and still is, an attractive young lady, who had no shortage of male attention. She herself does not shy away from confessing that she could have 'done so much better than him'. Ask her if she married for 'love' and you are met by her silence. It makes you wonder why a woman would put herself in that position when she has the freedom to choose her own partner.

I discovered that he was a successful, rather wealthy son of an affluent family and so obviously she would have no financial worries whilst she was trying to establish a career. He seemed a decent enough sort of guy and laid no restrictions on her, but she realised when it was too late that marrying for money just ends in heartache. She misses her single life, being able to do what she liked when she liked and how she liked. That is an argument that my friend Huma also uses.

'Why should I get married?' she says. 'I enjoy my freedom too much. I can do as I please, when I please and if I please. I don't have to tiptoe around someone else. If I want to sleep on the right side of the bed, I can. If I want to move over to the left, I can. If I want to sleep diagonally, I can do that too!'

Not only that, she says she would rather be alone and unhappy than stuck with someone and then unhappy. Like another friend of mine.

This friend met her husband online a few years ago. Both professionals and highly educated people, they went through the usual matrimonial search rites of passage and decided that they liked each other enough to get married. Had the full works, the whole over the top wedding package costing near to £25,000 and then … things just started going downhill. At six months pregnant, she tells me:

'He is as miserable as I am. He comes home from work and sits in front of the TV. We hardly exchange words; we don't even look at each other. We have become two strangers who just happen to live in the same house.'

Marriage does have the potential to make your life a living hell, but that still doesn't put me off the idea. I solemnly declare that I don't know what is worse; going to bed on your own or waking up alone. A few summers ago, I bought one of those gigantic mirrors that stretch from the floor to the ceiling and I placed it right next to my bed. They all laughed at me; looked at me as if I had gone mad or was suddenly vain. It was in fact neither.

The truth is that my room feels lifeless so I bought that mirror in the hope that it would bring movement into my surroundings. When I went to bed, prepared to climb into it, I would see someone moving around the room and it would make me feel that I was not alone; that there was someone there with me.

Do you know how soul destroying it is to think that you may never wake up the next morning and that you will have left this earth not having been loved by anyone? I sometimes think that if I died right now there would be no-one to miss me, no-one to want me back, no-one whose life would be empty because of me.

It is a lamentable reality that thousands of people out there do, in fact, happen to die alone. My father's sister died alone. She never married, never had children. Just spent her days in that one separate room, next to her mother, my paternal grandmother, and then died peacefully in her sleep. Knowing that history has a bad habit of repeating itself is not very comforting when I think of the possibility that I might end up like that.

Maybe people reading this are thinking that you don't need to be married to be happy, or indeed to even be in a relationship. That is true. But maybe I am a little old-fashioned. Maybe I like the idea of taking someone's surname and knowing that if I annoy him, he is stuck with me for good! I like the thought of living my life with a man who has shared vows with me, a man who will be mine, a man who wants to call me his. I like the thought of loving someone with all that I am, caring for him when he is sick, ironing his shirts, and being proud of him when he is successful and, when he is not, being that cushion of support. I like the thought of a man who knows that my heart floods with love for him and that, in a room full of people he is all that I see. I like the thought that he turns to me for advice and that my opinion is valuable to him. I like the fact that he respects my thoughts and my feelings and knows which dress I would like. I like the thought that when he reaches out his hand, he finds mine. I like the thought of being protected by him, and loved by him, and wanted by him and needed by him, and just him and no one else but him. I like the thought that when I am scared, just hearing his voice is enough to lift my cares away or that just to see him smile is enough to set off little fireworks inside. I like the thought of seeing my children exhibit traits of their father, and every time I look at them, knowing that I am married to the most wonderful man for whom I would walk on burning coal (… provided that I was wearing protective heavy-duty footwear).

I am not embarrassed that I am conditioned by fairytales or classic novels or even by the Hollywood romances. By the same token, I am not deluded by the 'happily ever after'. I appreciate how difficult a commitment marriage must be. It's just that living a carefree lifestyle where I had the freedom to float from one relationship to another never appealed to me either.

I remember once at high school, our form tutor asked us what we wanted to be when we grew up. (A question I am struggling to answer, even now.)

'I want to be married and have children, Miss,' I replied.

'What?!' she cried. 'You don't have *any* ambitions?'

She was a feminist who was allergic to the word 'marriage'. Yes, I did have ambitions and I went on to achieve much in my life. It's just that marriage and kids and family meant a lot to me too. It still does.

I guess I was just caught between two different worlds. In the Western context I was repressed for not wanting the Western lifestyle, and in the South Asian one I was too Western for rejecting the traditional South Asian lifestyle. It was neither of these. I was just misunderstood really. It was quite simple; I wanted marriage. The intertwining of two souls with Divine Blessing, that whole Ying-Yang phenomenon, it seemed attractive and wonderful, but I didn't want it the way those around me had it.

When I was in my early twenties, I wanted to get married. The problem was that, in my family, marriage was taboo simply because it meant that the dirty sex word would be a reality for me. A few times we had interest expressed for my hand in marriage but the parties were soon sent packing on account that I was too young. After that, the years kept flying by and I had an older brother who couldn't make his mind up whether he wanted to get married. In hindsight, it is obvious that he went through the same trials and tribulations that I went through and marriage was a word with which he also had difficulty. According to Pakistani tradition (well it certainly was in our household), you got married when it was your turn, and that turn was determined by your 'number'. Heaven help the poor sod who was the youngest in the family; if the older siblings weren't married, then the youngest wouldn't be walking in confetti any time soon. I was, and still am, the youngest.

I mentioned that I wanted to get 'married' a few times throughout my early twenties and I remember my sisters looking at me in disgust, like I was a loose woman wanting sexual thrill. They made me feel that I was dirty and that singledom was better for me. I didn't understand it then, but I know now that this made things more digestible for them. Their youngest sister was too young to get married; if she did then they would have to start treating her like an adult and that is something they all found difficult. Or maybe it was simpler than that. Maybe they just wanted to live their dreams through me? Whatever it was, they wrapped me up in cotton wool so much that it was a great shock to my system when I discovered that the world around me was neither fluffy nor white.

Then I stopped trying to fight with everyone and, in doing so, gave up the idea that in this vast world there might be someone who wanted to be with me. I wasn't mixing with men, partly because I didn't want to live a double life and partly because it was what 'bad girls' did. And so I shut myself away from the world for a few years.

When I hit my mid-twenties my father, who was the only one worried about me possibly spending my life alone, put the wheels in motion for marriage to be on the agenda. I think up to that point, I knew that I could kiss my dreams about a prince goodbye. I accepted that that sort of thing only happened in the movies and even if it did happen in real life, it certainly wasn't going to happen for me. My fantasy was my prince and all that I dreamed. My reality, however, would be what my sisters had had.

I cringed at the word 'marriage', or at least what it signified to me. Every time I thought of the Pakistani meaning to it, it sparked an awful feeling inside. But I couldn't keep running forever. It would catch up with me sooner or later, and when it did, I had to be prepared.

My father and I used to talk sometimes.

'I am worried about you,' he would say. 'Today if I am gone, you would have no one, no one will take care of you.'

As a family we didn't talk much; we all lived fairly separate lives, a family in name only. But one particular evening my father and I had a heart to heart, and even throughout those moments of silence, we understood each other. He said to me that he knew and understood that it wasn't easy for me and that he had no intention of marrying me off to some man that I didn't want.

'I didn't force any of them and I am not about to force you,' he said.

All he wanted was for me to take on board the idea of marriage; what it was and how being single would be meaningless for me. I am sure he said what he did bearing in mind the kind of life his sister had had. As much as I sat there trying to plead with him, he asked me to imagine what would happen as time went on and I found myself in old age. Who would look after me when I was unwell? I imagined myself in a nursing home, and suddenly the thought of being single seemed less appealing.

I explained to him my thoughts and he assured me that he would not let any *man with moustache* even contemplate marriage to me!

'Marry whoever you want. I don't care what colour he is, what he has, what he doesn't have, where he is from; all that I ask is that you marry a Muslim because on *Yaum ul Qiyama* [Day of Judgement] your children shall be resurrected[3] according to who their father was.'

My father is a great man, a devout Muslim. If you spend time with him, you would think that he is a progressive, liberal, intellectual type, and all the images you have of the *devout Muslim* would probably disappear in an instant. He really is a remarkable human being and sometimes all the bad things that ever happened to me or the pain I ever endured somehow cease to matter because I know that I am truly blessed with this wonderful man as my father. And if I ever have children, I shall be able to pass on those blessings to them for they will have his blood in their veins.

While I was there I negotiated that I didn't want some cheesy wedding film where the cameraman failed to understand the difference between 'zoom in-zoom out'. He agreed. I also requested that my wedding not be overtaken by 36,478 people whom I did not know. He agreed.

'I don't want any gold, Dad.'

'If that is your wish.'

---

3 The 'Resurrection' is one of the six tenets of the Islamic faith; that on a Mighty Day mankind shall be raised from the dead and held accountable for deeds, good and bad, whilst on this earth.

'Just my vows Dad.'
'You just find him.'
'I will.'

(Obviously an optimist in those days.)

Six: Send Me a 'Pic'

'You know what I really hate?' I said one evening, as Varsha and I sat down for our monthly *tell me what is going on in your life* meetings.

'No, but you are about to tell me.'

'I am beginning to hate the word *pic*. All these guys want a photograph. Why can't they say *photo*? What is with this *pic* business?'

'It's funny you should say that,' she replied. 'Punit is also looking and he gets sick of being asked for a *pic* too. He says that before even wanting to know anything about him, women go straight for the, *Thanks for replying to my ad. Here is my email address. Send me a pic.*'

From that day onwards, the word '*pic*' became quite a celebrity with us. Someone even mailed me to ask if I could send him a *pic* for his parents. Unfortunately, I wasn't hoping to marry any parents so his email ended up with the rest of the 'send me a *pic*' requests – straight in the reject bin. I didn't care how fantastic the guy was, using that phrase really began to make my skin crawl. Surely when people uttered that imperative, it was violating some international law some-where?

The looks factor is an integral part of the process and no one can, nor should they, claim that this is not important, because it is. However, I would like to believe personality should also count for something; otherwise we live in an extremely sad world. But this was the disparaging reality that I came to discover.

When I first started looking, the idea of exchanging photographs presented itself to be a major stumbling block primarily because I don't know how to smile (I kid you not). And photographs have a nasty habit of capturing you when you don't want them to. So I was stuck. I had absolutely no decent photographs to send to anyone. More importantly, my sister talked about how desperate women had become that they had to send their photographs to men – complete strangers who were all sorts of nutcases. The nutcase idea seems to be true enough, but my sister was from that old school of thought and, in her opinion (well what used to be an opinion at that time, before she learnt that being stuck in a cultural web was very much to her detriment), it was not the respectable thing for a girl to *display herself* by sending photographs to strange men. Exactly how she expected me to find a partner I never will know, but this instilled a considerable amount of fear in me.

I was already bringing shame by seeking someone of my own accord. Did I really need to make matters worse for my family by sending a photograph out to every Tahir, Dahniyal and Haroon? No. I could not risk that. So … I put my photo up on the profile for the whole world to see. The website people managed to persuade me with their little advertising gimmick that photo profiles received seventy per cent more replies and, quite frankly, it had been a couple of months now since I had started looking and everyone in my house wanted to know when they could put the order in for the wedding cake.

I also was aware that Auntie Reshma would soon be calling my house to ask my family whether they knew that their daughter was shamelessly registered on the '*In*-ter-Nett' and seeking a husband, since Razia who lived on her street has a friend in Bristol whose second cousin's daughter's son was browsing the profiles and came across my photo. Auntie Reshma is like a thorn in a certain part of the anatomy, and for all those who also know an Auntie Reshma somewhere along the line, my deepest sympathies to you all.

But the joke was on Auntie Reshma, because I had covered my tracks. On that particular website where I posted the photograph there was a section where it was obligatory to indicate whether the details had been posted by self or parents. For reasons of 'respectability', as well as to escape the infrared Reshma radar, I had ticked the 'parents' option.

The first response to my '*We are seeking a respectable match for our daughter*' was from a '*We are seeking a respectable match for our brother.*' I think there was a problem with the site, as they were under the impression that I was from the USA and 'living with brother and his wife'. When I pointed out that there was some mistake with the posting of the profiles and my profile number did not match the profile and description to which they were referring, the correspondent resorted to a slightly condescending tone. I don't know why though – I had made it clear that I was only seeking UK replies and it was not my fault that they were from the United States, or that the website was experiencing problems, or even the fact that he was meaning to contact someone else and accidentally clicked my profile.

After 'forgiving' me even though I was not to blame, the supposed brother of my potential husband had now become my potential husband. It was no longer, *'We are seeking a proposal for our brother'*, but more something along the lines of *'I am interested in your sister for myself.'* Once more, even greater confusion, as I had stated that I was my own parent and not my own sister! You may be surprised to know that I did not marry this man in the end.

Maybe I should have pursued him because my worst nightmare came true. Even though hundreds had viewed my profile no one contacted me. Then came one reply:

'Your daughter is *ma sha Allah* [by the Grace of God] beautiful.'

He was from the States but I really didn't want to start anything with someone from abroad. The mere fact of going further than Watford was bad enough as it was, so the thought of having to cross water, and lots of it, to go and see friends and family was giving me high blood pressure. Besides, he was the only one out of hundreds who thought that my *daughter* (who was actually me) was beautiful; surely there was something wrong with him. It was disheartening that I was deemed unattractive and that no one else replied, but the fact that this man was able to see past the looks thing was a comfort; maybe there were men in this world who weren't obsessed with physical appearance.

Perhaps I should explain something here. You see the photo that I had posted was a natural photograph. I deliberately did that and refused to send one where I was all 'made up'. Men didn't send photos of themselves wearing make-up therefore I didn't see why women should. I wanted the man who would be spending however much of his life with me to first see what he would be waking up to every morning. Anyone can look breathtakingly beautiful with cosmetics, but I wanted my man to be happy with me just the way that I am. I wanted a man who wanted me for me, not for what I could look like. A man who found me interesting and endearing and intelligent and caring and honest and warm and alluring and sensual and a whole host of delightful adjectives; he would be the one for me.

I was not a trophy and I didn't want to be seen as one. I am happy with the way that I look. I am confident and grateful for the way that I have been blessed. Beauty is beauty whether you hide it or show it and I wanted to be wanted for my real beauty. I am no supermodel but my greatest wish is that when I have lost what little looks I may have, I can still see myself and be seen as being *beautiful*. That is how simple it was.

Maybe I do live in a Utopian world but I believe that you can be stunning; however, that is worthless if you lack substance. At the opposite end of the spectrum, if you speak to an average looking person with great warmth, then you will find that the more you know them the more attractive they seem. That is why I never made a point about asking for a photo. Many times men offered but most of the time I preferred to just meet. In those instances where I did accept a photo, I was sending one too. I am not saying that looks were not an issue, because they are important; of course they are. Physical attraction is an essential ingredient in a relationship, but I preferred to know, first and foremost, how engaging a man would be on an intellectual and an interpersonal level. The looks factor was secondary to these. I think I was the only weirdo who went from *email* → *phone* → *photo*, whereas the norm was *photo* → *phone*.

'*Emails are laborious*,' '*I don't want to be mailing to and fro*,' '*Email is a waste of time*,' they would tell me. Perhaps these people were right, and I can understand their viewpoint too, but I suppose it depends on what you are after and what is high on your list. The first thing, or more of a priority for me, was the way that a man wrote. So you can imagine how pleased I was when I received this reply:

> 'I prefer e-mail at first, and if we find each other interest-
> ing, we could exchange photos and then even speak to
> each other!!!'

This potential husband was highly interesting and the best thing was that he found me interesting too (which always helps). We mailed a few times and I really got a feel for his character. However, he wouldn't speak with me on the telephone until I had sent him a photograph. This disappointed me slightly, because even if I had found him attractive, I would be reluctant to pursue anything with him if I had not felt any chemistry in his voice. A man had to capture me through his voice; this was imperative.

His refusal was disheartening but I knew and accepted that I wouldn't always be able to 'tick all the boxes' of that mental table of requirements that we have in our minds when searching for a partner. I was willing to compromise. I explained about my natural photo and he said that I could send him that *if I liked*. Well I liked and so I did.

Coincidentally, I was due to attend a friend's wedding that weekend. I knew I should have turned up with a placard stapled to my forehead saying, '*No. I am not married. And yes I know I am getting on a bit.*' It would have saved me having to answer that horrid question as to why I wasn't married yet and then sitting there pretending that the comments from people didn't bother me.

I must admit I looked *pretty hot* that day (completely objective and unbiased opinion you understand) and photographs had been taken. He asked me to forward those photos for his *perusal*. I was about to when I had a little think. After I had sent him my first photo, I hadn't heard from him. I was disappointed that an intelligent and polite man, as he had appeared, did not have the decency to drop a quick email as I had requested. Eventually, after prompting, he did reply, telling me that I had passed the 'first round of selection procedures' and that I should send him the wedding photos. Interestingly, he had not sent me his photo. We originally agreed that I would send mine and he would reciprocate. Only he failed to keep his side of the agreement.

It was then that I realised he had no intention of sending me his photo until I had sent him the wedding ones, and even then that would depend on whether he found them appealing.

Secondly, I had compromised myself too much, more than I had intended to or would have wanted. Surely, by sending him *super hot* photos, I would be defying the whole purpose of the natural one? The whole reason why it was so important to me was that that was me as my most simple self. Sometimes I walked around with no make-up, and I definitely was not one of those girls who refused to step out of the house or even open the door to someone without having the stylist to hand. Sadly, as I had originally picked up, the looks element was a pressing issue for him and he didn't want to pursue things until he was convinced that the woman on his arm would be the fantasy of all men. Unfortunately, I want to be the fantasy of just the one man.

'Just change your photo,' Varsha nudged me occasionally. 'It's beautiful, but you know now that men are different to us.'

'But Varsha, I adore this photo,' I always protested.

Perhaps I really was asking for the impossible. But deep down inside, I needed to know that there were people in this world who weren't obsessed with looks. Dozens expressed interest, dozens emailed and dozens even spoke with me. They would tell me what a good writer I was, how refreshing they found speaking with me, how alluring I was; but as soon as I sent my photograph, they never replied. Ignoring someone should be a criminal offence. If there is one thing I cannot stand (along with the word *'pic'*), it is when people don't reply expecting the other person to naturally understand that they are not interested. I hate that. Really I do.

We have had this discussion many times amongst friends and the general consensus is that they would be shattered if someone said to them, 'Sorry … I don't find you attractive.' But what is so awful about that??! We are never attractive to every single person, and if someone does not find you attractive, then it's not something to cry over. I think it's a great thing to be unattractive to other men but highly attractive to the guy who ends up with you. I used to always appreciate people taking the time to mail back. It certainly helped to move on without the 'what ifs'. At first, it was difficult to hear. A guy once mailed back and said, *Thanks, but no thanks.*' But as time went by, I became accustomed to the rejection and, surprisingly, it ceased to hurt. In fact, it served to strengthen me further. I knew what I had to offer. The physical was just a fraction of who I am and this made me even more confident.

Of course, this little experiment was also interesting at the same time. There was one guy who told me how much he had enjoyed speaking with me and that I was *a great laugh.* His profile had a photograph and it was only fair that he knew what I looked like. This was a fair point. But I also knew that our lifestyle and outlook on life was totally the opposite and that I would not be pursuing anything with him. It was only right to honour his request though, so I showed him the photograph on my profile. Surprise, surprise I never spoke with him again.

About four months later, he mailed to say that he had regretted his actions. He had thoroughly enjoyed speaking with me, and realised looks weren't everything. He said he seemed to be searching for me in almost every woman that he was coming across. Flattering of course, but unfortunately he wasn't my 'cup of tea'. I have lost count of the numerous individuals who have informed me that I was not their *cup of tea*. Well thank God for that. I would rather be someone's *'mineral water from a bottle'* than someone's cup of tea. (Don't worry, you will get your royalties ...) *Readers are asked to note that they will not understand the last sentence, but the one for whom it has been written, knows ...

'Maybe it's time to change the photo?' Varsha would say casually. But the more she suggested it, the more I resisted. I realise that I probably missed out on many good men through my stubborn approach with the natural photo but this was something about which I felt strongly. I would receive such wonderful replies from men but it would end when it got to the photograph stage. Like the time that someone from the USA had seen my profile, but because I had set the filters for UK replies only, he couldn't contact me. Then he created a new profile and changed his location just to get in touch. When he told me this, I was rather overwhelmed that he had gone to all this effort just to communicate with me. I apparently had captured him with my words and he was convinced that I was 'The O*ne*'. Then he saw the photo and I was no longer 'The O*ne*'.

I then reached a point where I just became fed up with the whole rollercoaster of it all. I decided to conform and send my photo with my first email. Since men wanted photo first, this is what they would get from now on. As expected, I didn't hear from anyone, but one day, I found an email sitting in my mailbox:

'Hey there, your au-natural photo was very impressive …
A little bit about me … well …'

He then went on to tell me about him. Of course I wasn't concerned about that. I was too busy trying to throw a party and distributing *laddu* [Asian sweets] because there was a man in the UK who liked my photo! Apparently, a female friend of his had decided that she would find him someone (I think as female friends we are too generous), so she had written a profile for him and posted it. When I replied, she had passed on my correspondence. I wasn't sure if I was comfortable with the fact that my mail was vetted, but it was ok; the guy didn't go into v-fib after seeing my photograph thus I was easily pleased.

I think sometimes you just know if that romantic barrier will never be crossed. We spoke a few times and although it felt comfortable, I had a feeling that nothing would come of it. He sent me his photograph and I wasn't attracted to him initially. I couldn't imagine being romantic with him. He had that *'We would make great friends'* look, but I was willing to explore. We met up and my instincts were right; it just felt illegal to think of the possibility of being anything more than just friends. We were also from two different worlds. He came from a very liberal background and had a love for Pakistan that made me uneasy. Having spent most of his life in schools all over the world because of his father's work, his outlook on life was different to mine. He couldn't understand how I was unable to just pack my bags and follow my dreams of going and living abroad. I think he saw me as a repressed girl who needed to liberate herself. But swinging from chandeliers was never my style. He had never been out with an Asian girl, especially a Pakistani, so I forgave his inability to comprehend.

By now I admitted defeat, accepting that I would not find anyone. And then my path crossed with one who had written in his profile, '*Thought I would test kismet to see where it takes me.*'

Well, kismet would bring him to me.

Seven: (Not) To Be

F ate is a funny thing. It will either slap you around the face or hold your hand and take good care of you. Whichever it is, one thing is for certain; it will always find you in the end. Somewhere. Somehow.

Having placed my first 'desperately seeking' advert, I checked to see if it was online. It was, and by chance I noticed the one directly above mine. It had been placed by another female and had been posted the day before. At the time, I knew someone that I thought she may get on with, and forever being the matchmaker, I contacted her to ask if she would be interested in meeting this person. We became friends and eventually she introduced me to a few friends of hers; that is how I came to know him.

We got off to a negative start. He made clear his disapproval of me and in particular, my criticism of certain aspects of the Pakistani culture. I had referred to myself as *British* once and he opposed that. He accused me of all sorts of things, especially of trying to be something I wasn't. I didn't understand what the issue was; I had said I was British (as that is what my passport said). I didn't say I was *English*, but somehow, for him, it was a crime to say that. I forced him to face up to a few home truths and of course, as I expected, he retaliated with personal attacks. For over a year, we had occasional contact and with the passage of time, I mellowed and fell for his words. I was naive and a fool; the latter even more so.

He was also seeking a partner and our friendship had now moved on. We were no longer firing nuclear weapons at each other. He showed me his matrimonial advert and talked about moving abroad and living a humble life. At first I thought it was because he wanted someone who was not materialistic and that this was a deterrent to see which woman could see past that. I approached him but found that he was 'speaking' with another. So that was the end of that. Months went by and we eventually lost contact.

Then I received an email from him one day and with that the channels of communication opened up once more. He asked to see my natural photo that everyone was rejecting. Weeks later, he asked me to marry him. Was this guy too good to be true? Was this the love that I had been seeking?

'Mein tumhey gosht nahin deh sakta. Sirf toh vaqat daal ka vaada kar sakta hoohn,' ['I cannot afford to give you gourmet food every day, but lentils twice a day I can promise to provide'] he said. 'I don't have a degree, and I don't have my own place to live and I don't drive a fancy car.'

'None of which matter to me; if you can love me, then that is all I need,' was my response. And with that I accepted his marriage proposal.

When I went to my sister's house to tell her the good news, I expected it to be tough. This was my sister who disapproved of almost everything I did. There was so much taboo in our lives that we acted as if some things didn't actually exist.

'I am getting married,' I announced.

She looked at me emotionless as if I had just informed her of someone's death. Silly of me really; I think I expected, or rather hoped, that she would be overjoyed and put her arms around me and tell me that she was delighted. Hurt by her silence, I quietly got up from the kitchen stool to leave and then she finally spoke.

'What is his name?'

By now, I was outraged but somehow it didn't matter. Nothing mattered any more. No one could hurt me, for I had a man who wanted to be with me and he would spend the rest of his life with me. I knew that if I showed my hurt and pain at her lack of reaction that would only serve to ignite hatred for him. She didn't know him but it was as if she hated him already. Or maybe it was me she hated? Nonetheless I responded to all the questions that she began to ask, and after the Q&A, I left. I drove back, tearful. She hadn't even said 'Congratulations'.

I cried so much that night, but he soon dried my tears with promises of how everything was going to be fine and how he would take care of me. I knew that apart from him, I had no one. I would love this man as best I could because from this moment onwards, he would be everything to me.

The period of time that followed immediately after was quite exhilarating. Having set the date and gone shopping for wedding rings and furniture for our room, wedding preparations were in full swing. I knew that nearer to the date it would become overwhelming, so in the excitement of it all I packed my stuff in boxes that I would take with me. I even went and bought a television for our room. I didn't want my family to buy me anything. All of a sudden hideous looking cardboard boxes containing everything I owned in this world were everywhere in my room.

Seeing all this really made my sisters uncomfortable. The eldest slandered me for being a loose woman since I had *arranged* this marriage by myself and not consulted anyone, mainly the elders. This confused me slightly because I would be living with this man and not the elders. I just didn't want to go down the route that they had and wanted me to. And I just didn't share the love of the cultural rituals like they did. Why couldn't they understand that?

A few evenings later, my sister came to see me. Looking at the cardboard boxes stacked up high, she said:

'Don't you think you are taking this a bit too far?'

By wanting to get married and having found someone, I was taking things *too far* in her opinion. We had an extremely heated debate and I told her exactly how I felt, about the way she had treated me for as long as I could remember and the appalling way she had trodden on my happiness when I had gone to see her to share my good news. She apologised and told me that she didn't know how she should have reacted and promised that from that moment onwards she would support me. Little did I know that in time I would need to call upon this promise in more ways than I cared to imagine.

After the initial romance was over, things changed. The differences began to leap out and we both started to feel the cracks. I tried to speak with him about it, how I felt uneasy but he just accused me of being negative. Then there came a point where I just didn't feel safe expressing my point of view. Eventually, it would only be laughed at and belittled by him. At first it was harmless, but then I started to take it personally, especially as he compared me to a friend of his.

Every time he did this, the smaller I felt. This friend he had known for quite a while and she, he said, was a remarkable woman. The first time he spoke about her, she did sound like a lovely person. But the more he talked about her, the more I withdrew from him emotionally. Suddenly, I felt inadequate. His talk about moving abroad and raising children there began to suffocate me. The whole idea of marriage began to feel like a life sentence. Having my whole life planned out for me, where I would not get a say, was not something I wanted at all.

All those things he wanted, they weren't what I wanted. I had known that we were different in our lifestyles, but I thought there would be some sort of compromise; I mean how else is a marriage supposed to function if only one person gets their way all the time? He laughed in my face and told me how his friend was willing to give up all she had and live a humble life of next to nothing and yet I couldn't. For her, there was no *compromise*. She wouldn't even dream of asking for a compromise from him.

Gradually, we started to argue more than we actually exchanged pleasant words. Relationships are never meant to be easy, and I was prepared to do whatever I could to make it work, but my needs were never asked, they were assumed. When I tried telling him this, he would attribute it to the fact that I was well educated. He said that that was the problem; education had corrupted me. He wanted me to be *Islamic*. As far as I was concerned, I was as Islamic as I wanted to be. But I wasn't like *her* and that was the problem. For him, there was only one interpretation of 'Islamic' and *she* was it.

By this stage, I had become sick of hearing about 'her'. Up until then, I refrained from protesting simply because she was his friend. I wanted him to share his thoughts with me. If there was something on his mind, I wanted him to feel that he could speak with me about it. After all, we would be spending the rest of our lives together and if he couldn't talk to me, then who would he be talking to? This situation, however, was spiralling out of control.

She was all he ever talked about. How wonderful she was, and I wasn't. How great she was and I wasn't. How fantastic she was and I wasn't. I once asked him why he wasn't marrying her instead of the un-wonderful, un-great and un-fantastic me?

'I can't marry you,' I told him one night. 'I cannot be that woman. I can never be like her.'

'Don't worry about her. She is gone from my life,' he said. 'As long as you promise to work on yourself that is all I ask.'

He was able to diffuse even the most awkward of moments with his charming demeanour and although on the outside it was kissing it better, deep-rooted resentment gathered momentum beneath the surface. What kind of a response was that? – *'As long as you promise to work on yourself.'* What was wrong with me? There was nothing wrong with me. Yes, I would develop as a person, as a human being, as a woman, as time went by, but how and in which direction I was headed was surely my decision? What was wrong with accepting me the way that I was? Why did I have to change to be acceptable to him?

These were all questions that continued to ferment in my head and I was unable to articulate. I was starting to feel increasingly choked. I told him that once and he got offended. His intensity was too much for me to handle. He always wanted to be talking to me. He actually didn't talk much and I had to carry the conversations, and I may be a woman but even women sometimes get sick of talking! He began to take that as something personal but I told him that I needed my space, in the way I would give him space.

'We can't be joined at the hip all the time,' I would say. 'There needs to be a part of your life which doesn't include me, and I want the right to have a part of my life which has nothing to do with you.'

How else would we survive otherwise? Surely we would appreciate each other more by having a healthy distance between us?

'Well, in my definition of husband and wife, we spend all our time together,' he would say.

The only thing was, we weren't husband and wife, and if this is what the characteristic of our relationship would be, then that was worrying. He would accuse me of being too independent and headstrong, with a *Western* mentality.

The anxiety of this situation just deepened within me but there was no one with whom I could discuss this. Varsha was in the middle of getting married herself and things were happening so fast that it was difficult to identify how I felt and what I felt. Furthermore, by now, I had been increasingly conditioned to rubbish my own thoughts and feelings and the idea of having a right to them became alien to me. Not only that, there were personal issues; things that I had buried deep inside me and hadn't dealt with in my life. He came from a close-knit network of cousins, and I had grown up lonely, just within the confines of my own home, so to me 'family' was a scary word.

The few times that Varsha and I did try and catch up, we both attributed it to be a severe case of cold feet. Yes. *That is what it must be*, I convinced myself. But as the days flew past, it became increasingly difficult. Everything just seemed to be plummeting downhill at an alarming rate.

I went to purchase the ring that we had picked out, only to find that there had been a labelling error and that the actual price was greater than we had been led to believe. This was a nuisance because I had been overjoyed that finally I had liked something. I had been conscious of the price, not wanting to burden him with something he couldn't afford and this had been reasonable. But the actual price for that ring was beyond what we could pay. After a major uproar at the jewellers, I reported the matter to Trading Standards and weeks went by before I was offered compensation, to be able to buy the ring at the price that I was originally expecting to pay.

By the time the letter from Customer Services arrived, there was no need for a ring. We had reached that point in the relationship at which it just fell to pieces and was irreparable. Perhaps we both knew, but neither wanted to admit, that we were just going through the motions. What little foundation we had had in the past had now crumbled. The bricks were robust, but the cement was not strong enough to hold them and so with the storms, the delicate structure would give way.

He had almost dehumanised me or, at the very least, refused to accept the human that I was. Consequently, my whole attitude just changed. The thought of marriage came to repulse me. Everything I said, he dismissed without reason. Suddenly, he didn't like the way I dressed. He didn't like my hair; although just below shoulder length, it was now too short for him. The way I spoke Urdu was unappealing to him. Her accent was better. I was also overweight in his opinion, and he made sure he told me this all the time. What started off as a joke now began to hurt. I asked him once whether she was overweight.

'No,' he replied. 'She had the perfect body. You couldn't tell that she was a mother of adolescent children.'

Even my conversation wasn't interesting enough for him anymore. Once at 2 a.m. he rang and told me that I didn't intellectually stimulate him. At 2 a.m. I didn't think that many people could even if they tried.

'But she could,' he said. 'She always knew how to. She would take a look at a bowl of fruit and relate it to Islam. She was amazing.'

Well if she was so amazing then what on earth was he doing with me? And if I was not intellectually stimulating to him, then did he stop and think that he may not be intellectually stimulating to me? He told me that he didn't talk much, and that she would always keep the conversation going. I told him that at 2 a.m. I couldn't care less and then I put the phone down.

I don't think he ever forgave me for that. I detected hatred for me in his voice that night. He hated me challenging him, yet he would always tell me how much she challenged him so I could never win. She may not have been physically present in his life, but in our relationship, she was there; very much alive.

I think the first time I had a slight suspicion that this 'friend' was not just a friend was when his mother asked me if I knew her. *Why would she ask me that?* Initially, I wasn't bothered. She did sound a lovely woman and his mother was friends with her. That is what friendly people did right? … They were friendly with those they met? Soon it became obvious though that they wanted to ensure that our paths would never cross. These hints were just part of a major storm that brewed every few days and worsened nearer to the date of when our families were due to officially meet.

The morning before his family came to see mine, I sat in my garden, alone with my thoughts. It dawned on me that this would no longer be my home. I would never be able to call it or see it as 'home'. I thought about what he was offering and it petrified me. Months previously, it had scared me, but now, it was terrifying. Whilst I accepted that marrying someone does constitute a major change in your life, and change was not something I was comfortable with anyway, the life he was offering me meant that I would have to radically transform myself. This was difficult to contend with.

I had been raised without restriction. I was free to make my own choices and there was never that element of *you must do this, you must do that*. My father had always given us the choice. Granted, he would make his opinion and his preference be known, but at the end of it all, he would always trust our judgement. And if we failed, he said it was no big deal, but a valuable learning experience.

When I was at university, in my final year I shared a flat with three guys. Anyone who has ever been in that position will understand how campus accommodation is so much better than private accommodation and how easy it makes life to be within reach of the university when you are doing your finals. I would leave my halls and be at the lecture theatre in less than four minutes … now for someone like me who has difficulty being on time, this is a godsend!

My sister was vehemently opposed to this even though there would be two other girls in my flat and I had an ensuite bathroom.

'Dad will never let you,' she said.

I approached my father and explained that if he objected I would have to look elsewhere. This was the only room that had been allocated to me and I was lucky, as most I knew weren't fortunate enough to have been granted campus accommodation.

'I know my daughter and I trust her,' my father had said to my sister. 'I have no objection to your living arrangements,' he told me. 'This is your final year and you are the best judge of what works for you.'

My father and I didn't speak much but when we did, he always left me with a tear in my eye. For me, he is the best model for raising children and I am proud of the way that he raised me. Naturally, I want to raise my children in a similar manner. My husband-to-be, however, had very different views on raising children and these were the direct opposite to mine.

During this turmoil, I remember the tears; I remember them well. I didn't care what kind of life I had to live, but I would not subject my children to it.

I began to resent the thought of having children with this man.

'Do you think that I am going to raise my kids in this country?' he would say.

His plans were to go and raise them abroad. Maybe Pakistan or a 'Muslim' country and build an orphanage there. When I argued with him, telling him that in my opinion there was no *'Muslim'* country, he accused me of being anti-Islam. I was criticised for being untrue to my roots by loving Britain.

'But this is my home,' I would say.

'But it's not mine,' he would reply.

If I was unable to respect him, then neither could he extend any sort of respect towards me. I was well aware of the differences between us, but foolishly thought that, as adults, we could enjoy those differences whilst uniting on our similarities. How wrong I was. It turned out that nothing about me appealed to him. Everything about me was wrong. I was not *her*. And that is what the problem was.

For years I had hated the idea of work, all I wanted was to stay at home and raise a family. Now that I was on my way to doing all that, I just wanted to run from it. I wanted to work and so push the date further on by six months perhaps, maybe even a year, as there were things I wanted to do with my life. All of a sudden I wanted to go abroad and fulfil my dreams of living there. I couldn't explain to him what I was feeling. I just wanted to go far away; somewhere where no one would know me. The more I tried to speak with him, the worse it became. He just gave me ultimatum after ultimatum and I was caught between him and my dreams. Where once upon a time he had been part of them, he was now apart from them and so I began to withdraw.

I know that it was probably difficult for him too, that is presuming that he felt something for me. I didn't mean to hurt him by my withdrawal, but somehow everything was my fault and I got sick of fighting.

I was torn. On the one hand I wanted this; he was a good man, he had many good qualities about him. We were once walking past someone who was selling roses. The man approached us and he bought me a rose, then we walked off. The man came up behind us and gave him his change as he had given him money for at least five roses, but he didn't take it. I think the rose seller was so touched by that gesture that he gave me another rose. '*That is a good man you got there,*' he told me.

On the other hand, though, I was not happy with what he was offering me. He was offering to make me a wife and mother, both of which I wanted with all my heart, but both of which came with too many conditions. I would have to stay at home, with which I had no problem, but then he started laying down restrictive rules and the more he did this, the more I retaliated.

Probably the one thing that was like a thorn was the fact that I used to write on an Internet bulletin board. This he hated. Often I would get people mail me and tell me how much they enjoyed my posts. But this he despised.

'After marriage, you are not going to write on there,' he said.

He wanted me to take a more *behind the scene* role, which summarises well the sort of life he had planned for me. I remember, once, pleading with him, as I was not prepared to stop writing. What started off as a firm protest ended in tears, for he always managed to break me no matter how much I resisted.

'You can write children's stories,' he told me.

I didn't want to write children's stories. I enjoyed writing what I did and it was immensely satisfying when I would receive mail from complete strangers, male and female, telling me how much they loved my writings. Yes, I would get marriage proposals coming through from men who were intrigued by me and my words, but surely that would be flattering to him in more ways than one. Firstly, that my writing was something of which he could be proud. Secondly, even though I was a sought after woman, I chose him. He obviously had no faith in my loyalty to him, which was rather sad, as I pride myself in the fact that I am an exceptionally loyal woman. All of this was meaningless to him though.

At the time, I was in contact with a few male friends. I think more than anything they were online friends. He was against this too.

'No male friends,' he said.

I could understand his viewpoint, but why didn't he trust me? If I had felt that these men had ulterior motives, I would have stopped contact immediately. They respected me and we were part of a greater circle of friends that consisted mainly of females.

'I will stop all contact with females,' he would say.

'But I don't want you to,' I would reply. 'I don't want you to stop living your life just because I am in it. Marriage is supposed to enrich your life not box you up in isolation from the rest of the world.'

I didn't have a problem with his female friends. I wasn't threatened by them. But no matter how I tried to explain that his friends were his friends and that a couple needed a network of friends in some guise or another, without which we would end up suffocating one another, the more he dismissed it.

'Yeah, if we have an argument you will find yourself in someone else's arms and then that is it.'

Not necessarily. I would hope that my love, commitment and the strength of my relationship would be worth something. But nothing I said made a difference. He just wanted to imprison me and by doing that he was only serving to make me miserable and my misery made his life a misery.

He told me that I would have to be covered after marriage. I cringed at the idea of 'hijab'. *Hijab* is commonly the term for the headscarf worn by some Muslim women, but I define it as a collective attitude of modesty. *Hijab* is reflected not just in appearance but in manner of conduct, I think. But back then, oh how I hated that word and the idea. *She* 'wore' *hijab* and had done for a year or so. It was 'racism' in her workplace that stopped her wearing it earlier. I hadn't asked for justification, but justification I was given. So, *she* 'wore' it, therefore he expected me to 'wear' it too.

I was a free woman and he wasn't going to make me 'wear' it. What else was this *hijab* thing if not a means of oppression? There was no way that I was going to listen to his demands. I never listened to my own father; did he really think that I would listen to him? I didn't understand what *hijab* was, and the way he explained things to me, the more I retaliated. I had in my mind my own preconceived ideas as to what it was, but the more he talked about it, the more I was against it. I was against it not because it was part of my faith, but because of what it represented to me and, especially, the way that *he* presented it to me. I knew what kind of life he would impose upon any daughters that we would have had.

'You will let my daughters go to university, right?'

'Of course.'

Then he would go on to tell me how it would be some *women-only* university in Saudi Arabia or something. This was

NOT what I wanted for my daughters. I wanted them to have a choice; a choice of the kind of life they wanted.

Another thing that scared me, which went back to freedom of choice, was that in his wider family, no daughter (except one) was beyond the age of nineteen and unmarried. They had a tradition of marrying the girls off at a very young age. Now this is something to which I fiercely objected. When we argued he would always tell me that I was Islamaphobic. I just didn't agree with his version of Islam. That was all. It didn't make me a *bad* person in my opinion. His approach did nothing more than make me build the highest of barriers, which, although protecting me from him, also resulted in me burying myself alive.

I would not be allowed to go anywhere on my own. I wouldn't be allowed to drive any more. And I wouldn't be allowed to wear Western clothing. Everything else I could just about handle, but the clothing rule really broke the camel's back. I couldn't imagine wearing Asian clothes. I hated them. I had gradually begun to get rid of all Asian attire. But the more he made an issue of this, the more I argued. Why was what I wore such a big deal? I didn't wear obscene, 'unacceptable' clothes. I didn't show any flesh, so why was it such a sore point for him?

In his eyes, my refusal to climb down from this made me too *Western* and *liberal* but I had to do this for my unborn daughters. There was no way that I would let them suffer. So I stood my ground. The more I stood my ground, the unhappier it made me. The unhappier it made me; the more I distanced myself from him. The more I distanced myself from him, the more he accused me of being too Westernised. And so we would go round and round in endless circles.

'*Islam this, Islam that*,' he would tell me. Anything we talked about was always around Islam and I hated it. When I asked him to justify his criticism of me, he bullied me into the ground asking whether or not I wanted to better myself. I had no problem with bettering myself. I saw Islam as being central to my life and I prayed, but I am sure it wasn't the way *she* prayed …

I wasn't just a Muslim. I was a human being first and foremost, and then a woman. Of South Asian origin, I was also British and a postgraduate. I came from an Arts discipline and I had varied interests. All these things made up who I was. I was a product of all that had happened to me in my life but none of that mattered to him. My achievements were meaningless in his eyes.

'She was twenty-nine when she went back to college and did that course. Now she is an established professional woman. Look at you, same age and you haven't achieved anything,' he once said.

This covert intimidation cycle went on and on and gradually eroded what little self-esteem I may have had. Varsha, at this time, had gone abroad for a while and so I lost my emotional support. I internalised all this hurt as it began to eat away at me inside and until it came to paralyse me.

People sometimes ask me if this is what it was like why did I ever put up with it? My response is that I saw him as my destiny. Things are never meant to be easy and men were meant to be difficult; they all told me that. Friends from all cultures and backgrounds would tell me that it was an uphill struggle at times, and this was something for which I was prepared. I couldn't give up at the first signs of trouble.

I had always said that I would put my heart and soul into my marriage, only here, I couldn't see it happening. This frightened me but I knew that it was something I had to face. I would speak with single friends and they told me of their plight and I remembered what it felt like to be single and lonely; those painful nights, lying in bed thinking that there was no one in this world for me. No matter what he was like, or how it was between us, he had many good qualities, and for me they outweighed his bad. He had his faults, yes, but who didn't? I had too many myself but surely when you care for someone, you accept their faults? That is what I tried to do with him but it was futile because still waters run deep.

There was one night that will always be etched in my mind. Even though this happened many years ago, every time I think of it, I live it all over again.

He usually called, every day, all the time; morning, during the day, and without fail at night. That evening he hadn't. I had spoken with him earlier that morning and he told me that he didn't feel too well.

'Don't go to college tonight,' I had said. 'Go to the doctor instead.'

'No I will be ok. I don't know I can't explain it, but I will be ok,' he told me.

There was a lecture that night and he had mailed me weeks before asking if I wanted to go. I hadn't, but he had and so he did. It was near to midnight and I was worried. He usually called but he hadn't so far. I wanted to see if he was ok. He eventually picked up and seemed *quiet*. I must have 'nagged' that he hadn't been to the doctor, because he assured me that he was ok, and he didn't need to.

'I went to the lecture,' he said, quickly changing the subject.

'That's good. How was it?'

'It was good. You should've come,' he replied.

The atmosphere was so tense, laced with an inexplicable unease. I couldn't understand what was wrong. Something was, but I didn't know what.

'... Farida was there,' he said after a long bout of silence.

'Ok ...,' I replied.

Silence prevailed. It was then that it hit me and I realised my own stupidity. I had been a fool all along.

'Why don't you just tell her?' I said, knowing that the silence had to be broken at some stage.

'Tell who, what?'

'I think you need to tell Farida that you love her, because you do,' I managed to say, trying to fight the tears that were waiting to erupt.

'You know how you've been unwell all day today?' He didn't respond, but I knew he was listening and so I carried on, 'Well you knew you were going to see her and that's why. And you're right; you didn't need to go to the doctor.'

'That is not true,' he protested. 'I asked you to come along.'

'You did, but you knew that I would never go to an Islamic lecture and so you wanted to cover your tracks, because you knew that she would definitely be there.'

He just listened. And then he started talking about her. Telling me things about her; what she used to say; what she used to do. I lay there in my bed, listening. I could almost detect a certain twinkle in his eye as he spoke about her, and I realised that he would never talk about me like that. When it came to me, it was always made clear that I wasn't good enough, that I wasn't a fantastic woman like her.

'You have to get to that level,' he would always say to me.

'What level is that?'

'Her level,' he would reply.

That night, as the tears just flowed, I remember telling him that I was not her; that I would *never* be her; nor did I want to be her.

'I am me,' I cried. 'Why can't you just accept me for me?'

'When she walked out of my life, she left a void in it.'

'And I cannot fill that void,' I replied. 'If tomorrow I am no longer in your life, then I too will leave my own mark that no one will be able to replace; nor should they have to, nor can they. You can't mould someone into another's place. Just take each person for what they are, because they deserve their own place.

He told me how much he had wanted to marry her but members of his family were against it because of the fact that she was over a decade his senior and had children. I think my reaction was something he really wasn't expecting. The fact was that I was neither a jealous nor possessive woman. A man had to be with me because he wanted to be, not because he felt he had to. This really touched him I think, for he confessed that all that talk about living abroad and running an orphanage, were all her dreams.

'What? ... Wait a minute ... You shared *someone else*'s dreams with me? ... You shared dreams with me that weren't even your own!'

Perhaps I was more hurt than angry. But so what? The reality had been there, plainly obvious. He didn't want to be with me and I couldn't make him; nor did I want to.

'Look, I want you to be happy. And if this woman makes you happy, then I will let you go. You mustn't pay attention to what the world thinks. Don't let society dictate your life. People will never let you survive. If you do something to please them, they won't be pleased; if you keep yourself happy, they still won't be pleased. So just take my advice and do what you want to. At least that way, you will be true to yourself. And that is the only thing that matters.'

'What about you?' he asked, like a timid mouse.

'Things happen ... And then you get over them,' I laughed, putting on a brave face because that is what survivors do best.

'I can't believe I am talking about this, and I can't believe that I am talking to you of all people.' Then he said he didn't want to talk about it and we left that conversation.

The next day, as part of his daily routine, he called as soon as he got into the office. This he did every morning without fail. We carried on as if that conversation the night before had never taken place. Weeks went by like this and there was a noticeable difference in our relationship. We weren't fighting. He was noticeably happier and was even helping me find a job because my contract had come to an end. He sent me various job vacancies and it was quite pleasing. I felt on top of the world. Maybe he just needed to get that out of his system and now we could carry on with our lives together without that cloud that had been overshadowing us.

I really appreciated his kindness, and I felt that we had reached an important milestone until one Friday morning. After the day of his last exam, he rang and asked to see me for *the last time*. A little uneasy about that, I thought he was being funny, but he had said it with such conviction that there was no room for humour.

I needed to see him anyway. I had gone shopping and bought a jacket for him. He had mentioned a while back that he needed one and didn't have time to go to the shops. I had gone out and purchased four from which he could choose. I had to make sure that the store would take them back; the last thing I wanted was to be stuck with four men's jackets!

We met up after work and I was wearing a business suit. Usually, when I met him after work, I would change from my business suit to casual. He didn't like me working, and seeing me in business attire would annoy him. But that day, I hadn't had time to change. He pulled up beside my car and I took out the bags. He didn't even see the jackets. I was so excited and had in my mind an idea as to which one he would like but he wasn't interested and said he would look at them 'later'.

He was acting all strange, nervous. Then he said that it wasn't working between us. I just sat there beside him while he looked at everything else but me. I remember thinking to myself that he was just a kid. He was two years younger than me, but at that moment in time, it seemed that there was a ten-year gap.

At first I thought it was a joke. That he was doing this to provoke a reaction. And then I realised that the joke was on me. He was leaving. One part of me wanted to kill him. The other just wanted to unite him with her.

'Go and get her and don't let anything stand in your way,' I said as I opened the door of the car and walked away. It would have been a perfect exit if I hadn't cried.

It is true. Sorry is the hardest word. Telling me that he didn't love me was what he could not do, but that is what I came to know, the hardest way. Every experience moulds us into who we eventually become and I learnt from this that if someone did not love you for who you are then that is not love. We used to debate the existence of *true love*.

'It doesn't exist,' I would argue.

'It does. And I am going to prove it to you one day,' he would say.

He did prove it to me. He got engaged to her days after he left me and they married in the weeks that followed.

Eight: Casualties of War

As I walked away and headed towards my car, it was if the sky had just turned black and my mind was about to explode.

What had just happened?
What was going on?
Surely this wasn't right?
How could this be?
He said he loved me.
This can't be happening.
What would I do?
What about the wedding?
He didn't mean this?
Surely he didn't?
Of course he didn't.
People who care don't hurt you.
Where did I go wrong?
How would I cope?
What would my family think?
What was he thinking?
Had I lost a real love?
Why was life so cruel to me?
Why was God letting this happen?
Did He not care?
Surely tomorrow it would be back to normal?

Who would I turn to?
How could I let this happen?
I must be a bad person.
I must be an evil woman that a great guy like that didn't want to be with me.
No one wanted to be with me.
What happened to forever?
This wasn't supposed to happen.
He said he cared, how could I not appreciate him?
You are being punished.
You were anti-Islam.
This is your fault.
Did I make this happen?
What about her?
Don't be selfish.
Don't stand in the way of someone's happiness.
No, this was the right thing.
He would find happiness with her.
That is what mattered.
You couldn't make him happy.
You can't make anyone happy.
No wonder you are single.
It's your fault.
Look at you.
You are fat.
He loved her.
It was your fault.
Please God, turn back time.
If only.

If only.
I promise I will be good.
Please make it all better.
Please let it be ok.
Help me God.
I am sorry.

Thoughts just buzzed in my mind as I drove out of the car park. He was in the car in front, and I could see him looking at me through his mirror.

You are not supposed to leave me, were my silent screams as tears streamed down my face. Was I expecting him to just get out of the car and tell me that he had made a mistake? Maybe.

I came home with a feeling of having just gambled millions and lost. All evening I waited for his call, but the phone didn't ring. His sister had come from abroad for our wedding, surely he couldn't do this? Once his stubbornness had subsided, he would be back. I knew he would. But the phone didn't ring. It was past midnight and I would usually be talking to him, but the phone did not ring. The whole night went by with me staring at it, expecting him to call. But the phone did not ring.

The next day I called him, to see if he had come to his senses. He did not answer. What was wrong? I hoped he was ok, he always answered his phone. This wasn't like him. I called him a few hours later and still no luck. I called him again and no response. Half an hour later, I called again. I wanted to see him. We needed to talk. I think I rang him about thirteen times, and nothing. (If any readers think that they can beat that record, then please do get in touch.)

He must have realised that I would just keep on ringing until he picked up. There wasn't a switch that you could just turn off. This was real. It was life. And it was going to hurt. If he had been unable to extend any sort of respect to me during the relationship, maybe he needed to now, for the sake of his conscience.

'I forgive you for what you said yesterday,' I laughed.

He didn't. 'It's over, don't call me again.'

I was in a state of shock, disarray and disbelief. I spoke with Rahila, who told me it was best to leave it, but was she even listening? When she tried to wriggle her way out of giving me his cousin's phone number, I asked, 'Is there something I need to know?' with a feeling that there was in fact something that I needed to know.

'They got engaged today,' she said after a long silence.

For that split second, time stood still. It really was the end. He was right. Apparently, everyone now knew about the engagement and it was as much of a surprise to them as it had been to me. As a group of friends, they knew about most things, but this had been very clandestine.

But how could this happen? He only left me days previously. I couldn't understand anything. Things were *normal* between us. On Friday morning, I received my usual first thing in the morning phone call. It was fine. Then at lunchtime, from out of the blue, his whole attitude had changed. How could he be engaged already?

I rang his cousin and he told me that she was adamant that she wanted to marry him. She. 'She'. The one who had come to haunt me, that s*he*.

'Trust me, you have been saved,' Shabeer consoled. 'I know my cousin and I know that he has a silver tongue,' he continued, 'They had a history, this would've happened sooner or later. Just be glad it's happened now and not further along the line.'

What history? There was no history! They were just friends! … Oh how naïve I was ….

Shabeer's words carried little significance. They were just empty words. I felt that my mind was melting and my heart crumbling. The events of the previous day and what was happening at that moment were like dynamite and my insides, a battlefield. The wounds wept and it hurt; unbearable pain flowing endlessly. Oh God, why wasn't it stopping? Why?

I spoke with Varsha and to be honest I cannot remember what happened. Did I call her on the phone? Did I go to see her? I don't know. All I know is that the next day she asked me to go to the movies with her. My heart had been broken and all she could think of was movies! In hindsight, this was just a means for me to leave the house and to forget the events and turmoil. Where would we be without all those who, from the goodness of their kind hearts, deem us worthy of their time and their thoughts?

I really didn't want to go to the movies, and if you were to ask what we watched, I couldn't tell you. I have no memory of the film. I cannot even remember sitting there in the cinema. All I remember of that day was when I met her by the ticket office. She was standing there with a small bunch of yellow flowers. She probably doesn't remember this, but I do, and when I saw the flowers, I cried rivers inside.

'You'll get through this, sweetheart,' she said and she smiled with sadness in her eyes as if somehow, deep down she could see my pain. Little did she know that this pain would only be the tip of the Titanic iceberg and that her shoulder would come to be a source of great comfort, a cushion for my broken tears for a very long time yet to come.

Over the next few days she would suddenly need my help and company. '*I am mopping the floor, come watch me,*' she would say. '*I am going to the gym, come and keep me company,*' '*I made too much pasta, come help me eat it,*' '*I need fabric for some clothes, come with me.*'

Varsha had decided that she wanted to learn how to sew. So in the evenings I would go round to her place and we would go through the basics. There was one dress we must've spent hours trying to make but didn't realise that the material needed a bias cut. It turned out hideously wrong! We laughed about it even though it was not funny at the time. She was intent on wearing it when she went on holiday in the weeks that were to come. Needless to say she didn't get to wear it! I don't know if it was deliberate but she made sure that I was kept busy. And for that I was grateful.

But no matter how hard I tried, she tried, we tried, it wasn't working. It was as if, in my mind, I was living in a movie, where the same scene was on repeat mode. The heartache just kept on coming in waves, piercing me each time like a sharp arrow; but as soon as the overwhelming feeling passed, I would feel all right again. Seconds later the same thing happened and so the pattern just continued. I kept blaming myself. I had been so heartless. The man said he wanted to be with me, he wanted to marry me, but I just couldn't love him back.

'Listen to me Nasreen,' Varsha would say, time and time again, 'This was not your fault, none of it. He loved her and she loved him. End of story. You were just the third wheel.'

No. Varsha was wrong. He loved me. He said so. Why else would he bring his mother to meet my family? The only reason he went after her was because I pushed him to her. No wonder he went; when someone's love isn't reciprocated naturally they will leave. I had to see him, tell him I was sorry, and that I could be all those things he wanted me to be. Varsha had warned me about this, that I would need to see him a few more times before I could finally let go. She referred to it as some *closure* business.

A few days later, I received missed calls on my phone. Hoping it was him, I rang most people I knew to see if they had called me. The answer was 'no' from everyone. It had to be him. Of course, when he rang from work, it came up as 'withheld'. See! He was ringing to tell me that he had made a huge mistake and that these days apart had made him realise how much he missed me and wanted to be with me. For all those sceptics who told me to stop my nonsense and stupidity, this would prove them wrong. Ha!

I gathered the courage to call him. He answered. Things were fine already. If he didn't want to be with me, would he answer his phone? No! No he wouldn't!

'… I just rang to tell you that I have still got that essay you gave me, and what did you want to do about it?' was his response.

He was doing an evening course and had asked for tips on how to write essays. I remembered that time I had stayed awake all night compiling a whole mini-booklet of advice and tips. As my father got up to offer *Tahajjud* prayer,[4] he noticed that the light was on in my room.

'Have you been awake all night?' he asked, concerned yet angry that I was sitting there wide awake surrounded by sheets of paper.

'I will sleep as soon as I have done this, Dad,' I promised before digging out an old essay from my university days and attaching it to the '*How to write an essay*' guide that I had compiled.

This is the essay about which he was ringing. He wanted to return it to me in case I might need it in the future. I told him that the best place for it was the bin.

---

4 *Tahajjud* refers to the last third of the night, just before the *Fajr*, the obligatory dawn prayer which is one of the five daily prayers proscribed for Muslims. In the Islamic faith, we believe that during this period of night, God's Mercy is at His Greatest, for He descends down to the lowest Heaven, out of Seven, and extends His Forgiveness for those who seek it. There are only two instances that God descends so close to man: once a year on the '*Day of Arafah*', during the pilgrimage of *Hajj*, and every night just before *Fajr* .

As the days went by, the cries in my head intensified with a little voice persistently reminding me that everything had been my fault. I came to live by that and transformed myself into an emotional wreck, vulnerable to the core; I was my own worst enemy. They were all worried about me, and who could blame them? I cried non-stop. At sunset, the pain would be at its most unbearable peak and my heart felt as if it was drowning.

Consumed by this overpowering emotion, I wept uncontrollably, ashamed but helpless as the children watched. My nephew, who was seven years old at the time, couldn't take it anymore and he came up to me, sat beside me and whispered in my ear:

'Please don't cry. I will take care of you.'

I was hurting but the worst thing was that, as a result, I was hurting those around me. And I blamed them all. They probably thought he wasn't good enough for me, and I lost him as a result of their behaviour.

When he came with the proposal to my house, it was a real nightmare for me. He was just supposed to come and see my father; that was it. But my sisters took over, like they would take over everything and the whole family plus the worm in the garden and all its cousins somehow found themselves *chez nous*.

Then, he had come upstairs to go to the bathroom, and my sister shot up like a bullet, suspiciously standing at my door, barricading me and saying that I was not to come out as he was in the bathroom and that I 'was not to have any contact with him'. *Contact*, for her, meant I wasn't even allowed to look at him.

'Did you plan this?' she asked.

Plan him coming to the bathroom? It was as pathetic as it sounded. Did she think that I would start having sexual intercourse with him on the stairs, or maybe in my room, because there was a bed there? Which century were they all living in?

Just because they had acted like lambs to the slaughter, not even showing happiness or emotion at the thought of getting married, didn't mean that I had to follow in their footsteps. If by getting married I had to follow that methodology and approach, then I really didn't want marriage. It was evident that they didn't think that marriage was for me either.

They were wary of the fact that I would be living with his mother. I could understand why, but at the same time, I thought it would be great. I have no problem living with parents, or looking after them; I consider that to be a duty. We all have parents, and we all hope that someone will look after them the way they would look after their own parents. When a woman gets married, how can she expect her sisters in-law to look after her parents if she isn't prepared to look after her husband's parents, should the need arise?

My married sisters couldn't understand that, and I couldn't understand them. I appreciated their concern that it would be difficult for me to adjust and about that whole *'daughter-in-law/mother-in-law'* war that we all fear, but his mother was wonderful and we got on well.

'I don't want to take your son away from you,' I once said to her.

And that was the truth. I wasn't out to separate anyone from anyone, nor was I out to hurt or destroy. As far as I am concerned, marriage enriches your life, rather than severing existing ties. For as long as I could remember, I had made a pact with myself that the family of the man I would marry would be something to cherish not to resent, because they would be important to him. They would be there when all others would leave. Partners walk in and out of our lives, but parents always stay. We can never repay what our parents give to us. That is why it was important for me to marry a man that I wanted and not one chosen for me; so that I could do right by him.

What my sisters wanted for me and what I wanted for me were two different things though and when his mother said a few things to me which I thought were unfair, I remember my sister saying, 'See, this is what you get.'

She told me that this was what she had warned me about and so I was better off single. Maybe they just didn't want me to get married, ever? Whatever the reasoning, I blamed them for not giving me the support that I deserved. They cornered me and I felt I had to choose between them or him.

Even Varsha was unhappy. She was concerned how he didn't even have G.C.S.E.'s and how, in the long run, the differences may prove to be detrimental.

'I know intelligence cannot be measured according to degrees and certificates, but I want you to have a good think about this,' she said. 'You are planning to do a PhD at some stage; would he support you, or in the back of his mind, would he be able to cope with the fact that intellectually, he isn't at the same level?' (I think she expected me to marry a rocket scientist. But how could I? Has anyone even seen those grey outfits they wear on the moon?)

Gradually, life came to lose all meaning and somehow the necessities of food and sleep drifted away. I came to neglect household chores as daily existence became a mountainous struggle, leaving my poor retired father to cook and clean for himself for months to come.

'She has stopped going to work, hasn't she?' I overheard him asking my sister. 'What are we going to do about her, how long can this carry on?'

I had been under the impression that he couldn't hear me, as I quietly wept into my pillow at night. Obviously, I had been wrong.

Going to work ceased to be an issue, as I was 'released' from my job. I don't think the employer wanted to terminate my employment because they gave me more support than any other would have been prepared to give. In the end, it all became too much and so they had no other choice but to let me go. It was a fair move on their part.

'Varsha, I am worried about her, we all are. Is there anything we can do?' my sister asked.

My family thought highly of Varsha. My father would say, 'She is a lovely human being. See the mercy and blessings

Allah[5] places in people? If we thought about His Splendour
the mind would burst in an instant.'

Naturally, as a father, he had a problem with a handful of
my friends while I was growing up. Those who wore a little
too much make-up; those who preferred to go out more than
stay in; those who dressed without a care in the world ... You
get the picture! He was a father after all and we expect that
from fathers. But with Varsha, I think if parents are not
supposed to like our friends, he certainly approved of her. If
he could've hand-picked a friend for me, he would pick her
every time.

'There is nothing you can do,' Varsha would say. 'Only
time can do what it has to. She has to deal with this and she
will.'

Everyone knew that only I could find that strength from
within me and keep going.

'You always say that the mind is a powerful tool. It is the
one thing that can be the nucleus of your success or your
destruction at the same time,' my sister would tell me.

Yes I knew that, but the emotions were immobilising. I
came to give up hope, feeling as if I had lost my purpose in
life; my will to live, my whole essence.

---

5 The Arabic word for God; the same monotheistic God of Abraham
whose progeny from one son, Isaac, gave way to Judaism and the progeny
of the other son, Ishmail (be peace to them all), brought the seal of the
Message with *Islam* meaning 'Peace'/'Submission to the Creator'.

'What is *wrong* with you?' my friend Tariq would ask. 'How can you let a man do this to you? Why do you keep telling yourself that you didn't appreciate him or that you didn't deserve him; ask yourself, did he deserve you? Did he appreciate you? When I first met you, you were this fantastic woman and he was a nobody; he couldn't give you anything, not what you deserved. You still are a fantastic woman, even through the tears and he still is a nobody. He knows it and he knew it then but he had to reduce you to his level to be able to control you. For your own sake and for those who care about you, please snap out of this.'

I refused to acknowledge the truth in anything he said. He had tried the caring approach but that didn't work; the understanding approach but that didn't work either; the gentle approach which failed too; the supportive approach which did not get very far either and the harsh approach which would have worked for anyone else except me. I was immune to everything. In the end it was he who gave up and not me. His friend made him realise that we all handle things in different ways.

'But I can't do anything for her, and she is hurting badly. I just want her to stop hurting. She will end up going mad. She doesn't do anything but think. It's as if she is still living in that period of time,' he said.

'Just listen to her, that's all you can do,' she had told him. 'She still needs to keep it alive in her mind, the wound is fresh and the way it's happened, it's hard on her.'

Bless him, he did listen. Even though he didn't want to or like to, but he did. They all did. What I failed to appreciate or realise was that although I was hurt to my inner dimensions, I was not the only one affected by this. If this was painful and difficult for me, then surely, those around me, those who cared, they also hurt from seeing me construct my own demise.

'You have got to pull yourself together, I don't want to hurt you, but . . . he didn't love you,' Rahila told me.

'But he did, he said he did.'

'He wanted to, but hon, the fact is that he didn't.'

'It would've been ok, once we would've been married, it would've been ok; he would've forgotten her.'

'Yeah, if you had married him, you would've both been miserable and he would've just seen you as the mother of his children, but his heart wouldn't have been with you. He didn't love you,' Abdah told me, time and time again.

'Stop doing this to yourself. The man didn't love you, please try and understand,' Shamas would say.

'I bet you, all those things he says to you, he wouldn't dream of saying to her. Even if you had done everything he asked, he still wouldn't have been happy, because he didn't love YOU,' Tariq said.

'You are this amazing person. How can you waste your precious time for someone who didn't love you?' said a frustrated Muniza.

'Of course he didn't love you. If he did, where is he now?' Shanaz asked.

'He didn't love you, Nasreen, and you know that he did not,' were Varsha's words.

She reckoned that I had loved him. I question that sometimes. Maybe it wasn't him that I loved, but more the thought of loving someone? After all, he made me feel insignificant; could I love a man like that? Who in their right mind would love a man like that? His mother had said to me:

'I don't think you love my son.'

'Why is that?' I asked.

'Because when you love someone, you do exactly what they want you to. You don't hesitate. I love him, and I would give up my life for him.'

'You are his mother, of course you would. But I don't agree that when you love someone you don't even question their wishes, and that you blindly do as they say. What if what they ask you is wrong, are you not allowed to question? Isn't love about mutual respect? Since when did it become one-sided? How would that work?'

Maybe she was right. But if my not jumping at his every whim meant that I did not love him, then so be it. None of that mattered though. There were hundreds of questions in my mind that I couldn't answer. Some of these questions I would never know the answers to. All I knew was that I had to see him again. At first he refused to meet me. Then maybe he realised that I had made it so easy for him and perhaps it was time for him to be a man.

When we met up, he was an entirely different person. He looked different. He was dressed differently. Even his whole collective attitude was different. Everything was alien to what I had known.

He asked me once, if, after we got married, I would take him shopping.

'Why would I want to do that?' I had replied. 'I don't want to change you.'

Sure, he dressed like an old man, and we laughed about it, but he liked the way he dressed and that was ok by me.

He said I hadn't made him feel wanted. I couldn't understand how changing someone's dress sense was making them feel wanted. Ironically, as we sat there, he noticed my shirt.

'What you are wearing is nice.'

It was along the lines of his definition of 'modesty'. Two weeks previously, I had been shopping. I decided that I should start implementing the changes that he wanted. All I had needed was time, taking things at my own pace and not his. I think that is what his greatest frustration had been; that things weren't happening as and when he had wanted.

'Little too late,' he said and then we went back to the silence as we sat there in the shade of that tree on that summer's afternoon.

'If my *Mrs* finds out that I came to meet you, she will go mad! She is an insecure woman as it is,' he said proudly.

She wasn't his 'Mrs' yet, but of course, mentally, she had always been. As I sit here and write this, I realise what a fool I was. How could I not see it? I haven't thought about this all these years but writing this and reliving the whole episode is making me realise how dumb I actually was. It was obvious all along. But then, I guess when you are in that situation things aren't always as clear cut. Maybe you genuinely can't see them or maybe you just don't want to.

'Why?' was the only dumb thing I managed to say. I knew exactly *why* but I guess I found it difficult to accept. I was owed some sort of explanation, some sort of reasoning which would serve to calm the buzz in my head. I needed something to stop the voices; the voices that were destroying me.

'Why couldn't you just listen?' he finally said. 'This wouldn't have happened if you had listened in the first place. It's your fault. This happened because of you.'

I was glad that I didn't hear the word 'she'.

'... *She* didn't put up such a fight,' he continued. 'And she didn't ask for what I gave you.'

'But I didn't ask anything of you.'

'I know. I did it because I wanted to. I gave you everything.'

Of course; how silly of me.

'You think I want to do this? You think that I don't think of you? I am only doing this because I have no other choice. I owe that woman everything. It is because of her that I am where I am today,' he continued. 'I might regret it years from now but I will do this. Her kids are relying on me. She is relying on me. And I am not going to let her down again.'

'You don't know what you are saying,' I told him. 'You are on the rebound from me.'

'When I came to you, I was on the rebound from her. Now that I am going back I am not on the rebound,' he laughed. '... I always wanted to know if I could get a woman like you,' he said quietly after pausing.

So all this time I foolishly thought that he wanted me for me when the fact was that he saw me just as a trophy. What hurt more was the fact that she had asked him what sort of relationship it had been between us. He said he had told her that I had meant nothing to him. As he told me this, he pulled a face, like he used to when he wasn't impressed with something. And as I sat there, I realised how little he thought of me.

'You've got nothing going for you. Sort yourself out,' he said. 'This will make you stronger. You will thank me one day.' He then got up to leave.

I couldn't let him. How would I ever be able to cope without him? For the last few months, he had come to be the centre of everything and now all of sudden he wasn't going to be around any more. He took me to the café and we sat down and he bought me tea. .. See! He did want to be with me. I am the one who he wanted to be with but I had made things difficult for him, and so he had no choice but to go for her.

A Sinead O'Connor track was playing on the jukebox and he signalled at it. I thought he was dedicating the words to me. Looking back and writing this, he was probably saying that nothing compared to her. Or maybe he was telling me that I would never find anyone as good as him. During that final meeting, he did emphasise that I should think of him once in a while, remember and reflect on what a great love I had tossed to the side. Of course he was right. This was my fault.

Well I had to fix this. I had to.

He was torn between two women. The one he wanted to be with and the one to whom he felt obligated.

'You are young, you are pretty; you have no baggage. You won't have trouble finding a guy. She is thirty-five; has children; is divorced, insecure and unattractive. I have to do this. If I don't, then no one will marry her. Do you know how difficult it is for her to find someone? I am marrying her for the sake of Allah,' he said.

'Marrying you would have been for the sake of Allah,' my father told me. At the time I didn't understand, like with most of the things that were happening, but now I realise how right Dad was. In fact the penny dropped just last week when I sat down to write this chapter. How true my father's declaration presented itself to be. By staying with me, he would've been doing me a favour and hence trying to gain reward from Allah by staying with a woman he didn't want. So in effect, by saying that, my father just repeated what my friends had said done all along – *he didn't love you.*

At that time though, what did my father know? What did anyone know?

I knew that he was marrying her because he felt sorry for her. I knew this because that is what he was telling me, and I believed him. He couldn't marry her just because he felt sorry for her. There had to be a solution to this.

We could get through this, he could marry us both. He was the one who always went on about living the *Sunnah*[6] and living for *the sake of Allah*. Well surely, this situation required that, and that is why the multiple marriage system was there. Muhammad (*sallalahu alayhi wa sallum*)[7] married the women who were divorced, widowed or considered as social outcasts and had no-one and nowhere to turn.

I wouldn't ask for much. I hadn't asked for anything so far, unlike the other girls he had approached for marriage who wanted a house and a car, jewellery, presents, holidays, all those material things that seem to make up life. The only thing I asked was for love in his heart for me.

When I first met him and we first spoke of marriage, I was scared of letting someone into my life.

---

6 Ways of the Prophet Muhammad (*sallalahu alayhi wa sallum*), his habits, teachings and lifestyle.

7 Muhammad (*sallalahu alayhi wa sallum*), the Seal of the Prophets; the Last and Final Messenger of Allah who reiterated the message brought to mankind by Adam, Noah, Abraham, Jacob, Isaac, Moses, Joseph, David, Solomon and the Son of the Blessed Virgin Mary, Jesus Christ (*alayis Salaam*; may the Peace and Blessings of the Almighty God, the Most Glorious, the Supremely Majestic be upon them all). Whenever the name of the aforementioned Prophets of Allah is heard, read or spoken, as Muslims, we say *'alayis Salaam'* [peace be upon them]. When the name of the Prophet Muhammad is mentioned, read or heard, we say *'sallalahu alayhi wa sallum'* [may the Peace and Blessings of Allah be upon him]. We believe that Muhammad is the Best of Creation and a mercy to mankind, and his name is engraved on the Throne of the Almighty God and that on the Day of Judgement, Muhammad shall be granted the Highest Rank in Paradise, for that is what God has promised him.

'If I take your pain away, Allah will reward me,' he had said.

Well this way, he could take the pain of both women away and Allah would reward him twice.

'I want to write to her,' I told Varsha. And she just looked at me. And she kept shaking her head. 'I was afraid this would happen; that he would lull you into a false sense of security,' she said.

What was she talking about? He had said he was marrying her because he *owed* her. You don't marry someone because you owe them!

'Just let it go. Please don't hurt yourself any more than you already are,' she said. 'See reality for what it is.'

Ignoring Varsha's advice, I did write to her, suggesting that he marry both of us. And she laughed at me. In my life, at that point in time, I may not have been as *religious* as her, churning out textbook answers, but I was proud for the little mercy in my heart. I distinctly remember telling him one night that if ever there was a woman out there who needed him, I wanted him to marry her.

'Why would you even say that?' he asked.

'You are a good man. If you can take someone's pain away just by being in that person's life, then you should,' I had replied.

But I soon came to know that people often hide behind the word 'Islam' to forward their own agenda and that theory is often distinct from practice and reality. He gave great speeches about Islam, but when it came to the crunch, that is all they were. I may not have looked 'Islamic' or talked 'Islamic' but my heart was no less 'Islamic' than hers. This puzzled me even more. She was supposed to be a great Islamic woman, so why had she laughed at me? I had been sincere to her because I respected her.

'I do not mean to hurt you with my words,' I said.

I had poured my heart out in that email. It had taken me days to write. Yet within the hour came a stern reply from her.

'He is free to marry whomsoever he wishes,' she said. She talked about the past and people being separated and reunited and then them being there to stay, but I didn't understand. There was no *relationship* between them. She was just a much respected friend; so what was she talking about?

'Ask Allah for help,' she told me. 'He is the only one who can save you now.'

She had sent her reply to me, copying him in. I don't think he ever got to read my mail to her. All he knew was that I had mailed her. He would never know what I had said.

That explained a lot of things because he replied back, 'I reiterate that I will not marry you, even if you wanted to be wife number two, three or four.'

This came from a man who had said that he loved me. Now I know that *love* is probably the most abused and misused word on the planet. Why couldn't he have said this from the start? Why couldn't he have just been straight with me that he loved and wanted someone else? Why compare me right up until the last minute and even then shift the blame onto me, making it out as if he was just marrying her out of obligation as a result of my actions? I wasn't a bad person, why did he have to be so cruel?

He accused me of trying to cause trouble and split them up, and this hurt more than anything else. For those who know me, being malicious is an art I never mastered, so I wrote a final mail to him:

If after all this time you think that my mail to her was sent with spiteful intent, then you failed to understand the woman that I am and the one that I always was.

Thanks for finally being honest. Pity that is something you were unable to do all along. I didn't ask for much; just honesty as that is what I had to offer.

Don't worry this is my last correspondence to you.

Be happy.

As God is my witness, I really do wish that they have both found much happiness in each other. Despite my affliction, I am proud that in the end their love became a reality and that perhaps in some way I was able to help him gather the courage to stand up to society and be with her.

I found out many truths afterwards. So our few months' encounter really did turn out to be nothing to him; as had everything to do with me.

Of course when something doesn't break you, it just tests your endurance and you become stronger and better for having experienced it. Even though this was the worst experience of my life so far, it was also the best thing that ever could have happened to me. It moulded me into the woman that I am now, and for that I am glad. Like a candle that starts off strong, but which melts after it has been lit, this experience would destroy me. However, the beauty lay in the fact that the flame cannot last forever, and after its appointed time, after it has melted the candle, it too extinguishes itself. After the flame did its damage and the melted wax cooled and hardened, taking a new form, this experience sculpted me in a way that I never thought possible.

God works in mysterious ways – He sure does. And despite being a casualty of war, I was victorious. By subjecting me to this trial, my Creator honoured me and, as far as I am concerned, there is no success greater than that.

For any person who may be going through something similar, you may find the following advice enlightening. The Noble Book of Guidance, the Qur'an[8] contains verses which

---

8 '*Al Qur'an* [the Recitation]. For over fourteen centuries, billions around the world from diverse cultures and walks of life have turned to Al Qur'an as a source of guidance and wisdom, in matters of daily life, spiritually, emotionally, socially, politically and even financially.

It has been a timeless well of knowledge and inspiration for scientists, artists, historians, philosophers and mathematicians. It has been a cushion of comfort for dreamers, lovers, believers in God's Oneness and Power and all those who hold a hope for world justice and everlasting peace.

Those who have never been exposed to or opened up their minds and hearts to the Divine Words of the Recitation; may not recognize it as a revelation from the very Being Who created all things. Those who have experienced its miraculous nature hold it as a treasure; hold it as gift, from

narrate the diversity of mankind, of cultures and of languages. This diversity exists because of the diversity in the individual. The Creator (whether you believe in Him or not) has adorned every soul with a unique fingerprint. Even identical twins will not share a fingerprint. We are unique. We have been created unique. And we are meant to be unique.

So don't let anyone ever tell you any different.

Nine: Lean on Me

'When we honestly ask ourselves which persons in our lives mean the most to us, we often find that it is those who, instead of giving much advice, solutions, or cures, have chosen rather to share our pain and touch our wounds with a gentle and tender hand. The friend who can be silent with us in a moment of despair or confusion, who can stay with us in an hour of grief and bereavement, who can tolerate not knowing, not curing, not healing and face with us the reality of our powerlessness, that is a friend who cares.'

(Henri Nouwen)

Will I ever forget that when I rang Shanaz, she would always answer with a smile, no matter how difficult her day may have been? *'Come around right now,'* she would say without me even asking if it was ok to do so. Will I ever be able to forget those nights, sitting up with her until the early hours of the morning and her comforting me, even though she had to go to work early the next day?

Will I ever forget those endless nights that I cried and Abdah listened and supported, sharing my pain? How many times did I wake her up from her sleep at ridiculous times in the night, at dawn, because I thought I was going to die? Too many times. And how many times did she say to me, 'Don't

call me, I need my sleep,' or 'Don't call me; you are annoying'?
Not once.

And what about the beautiful bouquet of flowers that
Shamas sent me? '*Stay with me for a few days, and if you want to talk
about him all night, we can do that too. We won't sleep,*' she had said
even though she had just had a baby and was still trying to
recover from the caesarean.

And what of Tariq's sweetness, that he contacted a girl he
said he never would again, just so that she would speak with
me and give me Islamic guidance on how to cope.

And what about Varsha, who would always make time
during her busy day to give me a quick call to see if I was all
right? '*I am giving you suicide watch,*' she would say. '... *We will
laugh about this in years to come.*' (And so we did.)

'You may have lost a guy, but look at all those that are in
your life because they want to be; because of who you are as a
human being,' Tariq once said.

At the time all this meant very little to me and I apologise
sincerely for not knowing how precious my friends were. I
dedicate this chapter to all those people who, through their
friendship, made me realise that I was truly blessed.

Friends who, from worry, told me I looked worse than
their grandmother as I lost weight, going from a size twelve
down to just over a size six. (Shanaz, I will always remember
the way you felt, and after a year or so, how proud you were
when I started to eat properly and use Oil of Olay!)

Friends who, out of compassion, were able to forgive my
constant raving like a broken record. And who found it in

their hearts not to distance themselves from me as a result but instead felt, and shared, the severity of my pain.

Those friends who, out of their busy lives, found the time for me at the most awkward and most inappropriate moments, rallying around me when I was at my lowest, living the days for me when I found it impossible.

Friends who managed to see some goodness in me, when I believed that I had none left; friends who refused to let go of my dignity and self-esteem even when I showed them the door; friends who picked up my tears and held them tight so that I wouldn't drown in them; friends who heard those silent cries in my heart and tried to protect me from my own insanity; friends who went through the emotional spectrum of anger, acceptance, hope, despair, fear, pain and hurt on my behalf, when I was unable; friends who refused to give up on me, showing me that I could and would find it deep within me to carry on and survive.

I dedicate this chapter to friends; friends everywhere.

Friends who are sent to our lives to get us through the bad times;
Friends that we lean on;
Friends who lean on us;
Friends who make it worthwhile;
Friends who see when we are unable;
Friends who hear when we refuse;
Friends who feel when we are immune;
Friends who share when we are selfish;

Friends who laugh when we cannot;
Friends who believe when all faith is gone.

What would come of this world, if there were no longer friends?

A most loved verse of the Qur'an comes to mind:

'Faabi ayyi a'aalai Rabbi kumma tukazzibaan'
'And which of the favours of your Lord do you deny?'

(Surah Ar-Rahman, The Most Merciful 55:31)

Ten: So Strong Inside

After a hurricane tears down an island, the destruction that ensues has to be faced at some point. The inhabitants must go back to their now shattered lives and pick up the remains of what used to be, salvaging what they can in order to rebuild their lives.

Like one of those islanders, I too had lost all that I had ever known and I too had to rebuild my life from scratch. I felt I had lost my dignity, my pride, my essence of self, my whole will to live, my belief in hope; all that had ever come to define me, the woman, the human being that I am.

'The only thing that can get you through this, Nasreen, is your faith,' Varsha said. And that is exactly what came to be.

Although not a believer herself, Varsha knew that I have always been a woman of faith. Growing up, I had been a lonely child so faith gave me much comfort. If no one else cared, then at least God did. An often quoted *hadith* [saying, prophetic tradition] of Muhammad (*sallalahu alayhi wa sallum*):

'The world is a prison-house for the believer and paradise for a non-believer.'[ii]

This was most certainly true for me. I have always felt a prisoner in life. The world has been a source of great pain, and I have always dreamt of something better. At the time I was unfamiliar with the concept of *Paradise* except that about which I had been told, but those explanations had served no great purpose in furthering my understanding about the meaning of life and the universe.

In those days, I didn't even know what spirituality was and so I was content with being 'religious'. As I grew older, it became clear that there was a profound yet obscure difference between the two concepts but I carried on with life flitting happily between the two. Now, I have discovered that everyone seems to have their own ideas as to what constitutes being 'religious' and somehow they don't want to associate themselves with the stigma that it holds (especially if you are Muslim and living in the UK).

I have always had a connection of some sort with the One Who Created me. And those of us who experience much heartache from the harsh realities of this cruel world always tend to look towards a Supreme Being for answers that no one else can give.

Coming from the Pakistani background that I did, like many other Muslims of Pakistani origin, it was more a case of believing because that is what you were taught to believe, not because it made sense to you. However, the experience that you have read about over the last few chapters became a pivotal point of change in my life, and would turn out to be the catalyst of an amazing personal metamorphosis.

When things happen, things that we are not expecting, 'bad things', naturally it is a great shock to the system. We never quite understand. Consumed with the fear of the Unknown and forced to confront our own mortality, we become hostile to the change and unwelcoming of it. In tandem, we are unaware how beautiful and appropriate that change is. We cannot know this, as we have the inability to understand or foresee the future; this only lies with the Sublime Creator who is *Al-Aleem* [the All-Knowing].

I look outside my window as I am typing this and I will tell you what I see. I can see down the road opposite me. As is a common feature of most urban landscapes, the houses on that road are marked by trees either side. Last year, the council came and cut down the trees which had grown to such a height that they had become dangerous. It was feared that in the event of a storm, they would snap and destroy the houses nearby. Not only that; during the Autumn months they were shedding an enormous number of leaves, making it perilous for pedestrians and, of course, street cleaning had become difficult. Consequently, the trees were cut.

I, along with most people in the neighbourhood, thought that the council had destroyed them. We were so used to these gigantic and scary looking things that seeing these now horrible stubs was slightly alienating and weird. The real reason was that we weren't used to this; it was new and we were accustomed to the way the trees were before. However, we had to get used to it as there was nothing that anyone could do.

A year on, these trees are once again in bloom. Although now much shorter than they were, they look marvellous. They are in perfect proportion and the danger is no more. We are now all wondering how we ever put up with the other hideous trees!

Similarly, at the time, I couldn't understand what had just happened to me. I lacked the basic Islamic knowledge to put into perspective my pain and the reasoning behind it. Like those trees I was given help which seemed then to be inappropriate. This trial would serve to pave the way for a better outlook on life, and subsequently a more meaningful existence. My father always said that in times of trouble and despair, one of two words found themselves to the tongue of mankind: either he will cry out for his mother or he will cry out for Allah. Well I am one of those who cried for Allah.

Before any of this happened to me, I was very much living my life as a person without awareness of what my purpose was; why I was created; what would happen to me when I died – in sum what it meant to be 'Muslim'. I only ever used the word 'Allah' when things got tough or out of respect and fear of the Inexplicable. But this tribulation spiritually cleansed me and opened my mind intellectually. For that I will always be indebted.

I used to have my prejudices just like any person. I would see faith being practised around me, and I wasn't the greatest fan. I failed to realise that it was the cultural version of faith with which I had a problem and not the teachings themselves. Over the past few years I have been walking towards Islam of my own accord, but my encounter with Mr Wrong left me in a state of disorientation and served to undo all my hard work, or at least so I thought.

But when he left, I carried on following that same path with my own mode of thinking as opposed to his. I went on to discover, from my own research, an Islam which would leave me thoroughly enlightened and was contrary to the version that he wanted to enforce upon me. So the rate of acceleration on my spiritual path, as a result of this experience, was dramatic and something I could not have envisaged. I needed to understand what was happening and why it was happening and why God was letting this happen. Did He not care about me? Had He forgotten about me?

I needed to find out who God was.

I needed consolation. I needed help.

I needed to embark upon a journey and so I did.

Everything happens for a reason and that is precisely what happened; only at that time I didn't know. I think we all believe this adage, even if we don't believe in a 'Supreme Being'. But what I needed was to find out the reason and I wanted the Supreme Being to tell me.

Primarily, my first concern was how to do this and if I would ever be able to stop the heartache, the torment that was eating away deep inside. I had a thousand and one questions that I was addressing to God; questions that I was addressing to the Unknown, the *Ghaib* [Unseen]. I couldn't see Him. WHERE was He? He said He cared, but I felt abandoned. How could He forget about me? Did He hate me? Why was He hurting me?

I had always prayed because it felt right to pray, but my life was lacking in proper spiritual practice. When times were good I forgot about Him, when times were bad I cried out to Him. Although going through the actions and the motions, I was failing to fully connect with Him. My soul never felt as if it had ever fully surrendered and I needed to change this. Unbeknown to me, Vicissitude of Time would come to reveal all that I sought.

A few weeks before he left, when I thought that everything was back on track and that we had a newly found understanding, he had sent me details about a job. This job I had already seen and applied for as well. Extremely touched by his gesture, I thought he really did care, that perhaps my wishes and feelings did matter to him. Perhaps, finally, I also mattered to him, as he told me that he wanted me to apply for the job.

Of course, none of that was true. I was mistaken. I had been the whole time. The real fact was that he knew he would leave me, and so he wanted me to have something to occupy my mind, making the blow easier to handle. I suppose I should be grateful that he did think of me in some capacity.

'It was all planned,' Varsha told me, and she was right.

He had already decided weeks, maybe even months, earlier that he would leave me as soon as he finished his exams. When his final exam was over, officially that is when 'we' were over too.

My interview date came through a few days after we finished and so I went along, despite being in a state of turmoil. As I sat there, in the waiting lounge, a pretty young lady wearing a headscarf entered. If only I had just listened to him. This is all he wanted; he wanted me to wear the scarf and I couldn't do it.

Surely *hijab* couldn't be that bad if this smart young lady, in Western dress, was observing it? She smiled and sat down.

'What is it like to wear that thing?' I asked her.

She was a pleasant young girl and she started to answer my question. The more she spoke, the more interested I became. Although she gave me standard answers that I didn't want to hear, just being there in her company somehow made my heart soften to this piece of cloth, and I cried even more.

Up until then, I looked at women who observed *hijab* as 'oppressed', and a whole host of other labels. But as I sat there, I soon came to realise that you do not need to be covered to be oppressed. She was a medical student and from the way she spoke she was most certainly not oppressed. If anything, sitting there beside her, I realised I was the epitome of the *oppressed woman*.

The cloth that women wore had nothing to do with oppression; it was the actions of people that lead to the oppression. I contemplated my relationship with him, and realised that that was oppression, not the free choice to wear what you wished. If I had stayed with him and married him, and had he forced me to wear that same scarf, then that would have been oppression, not the scarf itself.

From my conversation with this free woman, I, the down-trodden repressed one, came to be invited to a gathering the following week. I had shared my heartache with her and I was asking questions that she couldn't answer. Maybe I expected this child, just over half my age, to answer questions that I would only find from further exploration and research of my own.

'Perhaps you may like to come to the event,' she said. 'Maybe you will find some sort of comfort, some sort of solace there.'

We exchanged email addresses and I forgot about it, not expecting her to contact me again, so it was a complete surprise when I did hear from her.

The venue for the gathering was one of the colleges of the University of London. I liked the sound of that already. They wouldn't force me to read the Qur'an and I wouldn't be expected to be *submissive* (… the stereotypical ideas and phobias we walk around with are amazing). If it had been at a community centre run by my Uncle Iftihaar, then I wouldn't have gone. That version of Islam I had grown up with all my life. I just wasn't interested. That is why when he mentioned Islam, in my mind that is what he meant and so I would switch off.

Naturally I had my reservations about this forthcoming event. I realised that everyone would be observing *hijab* (yet again, another of my own preconceived notions based on no evidence but my own impression and assessment) and I didn't want to be out of place. But then again, in my life, I never really fitted anywhere so it would be no big deal. Said the Messenger of Allah, Muhammad (*sallalahu alayhi wa sallum*):

'Be in this life as if you were a stranger or a traveller; on a path.'[iii]

Funnily enough, that is how I had felt all my life. I felt as if I was someone who didn't belong anywhere. It was as if I had been walking in the dark all this time, trying to find something. Not knowing where I was going, only knowing that I was alone. Sometimes I felt that there was light, but then soon after it would fade, leaving me to contend with the fear of the dark. Yet I carried on walking. Sometimes I would stop; rest a little, but I would have to keep moving on. And then there were times, like now, when I would step on broken glass that was in my path, and I would have to carry on while I bled.

When I turned up on the day of the gathering some of the women in that hallway were not covered; some were observing *hijab*, some were wearing the full *jilbab* [long, baggy outer garment] and there were even a few in *niqaab* [face veil]. I felt weird, awkward almost, and wanted to turn back and walk out. But then I couldn't go through life not facing things. This was something that I had to deal with and I was going to deal with it.

I approached the table, signed in and was 'registered'. The young girl, because of whom I was there, recognised me.

'I am glad you made it,' she said.

I smiled, not sure if I was glad though.

By that time, another young lady came in. She had just graduated from her dentistry course and my young friend introduced me to her. The dentist was wearing a *jilbab* and I didn't know how to talk to her. Was she going to force me to wear it? Would I have to say the word *Allah* with each sentence? Would they all make judgements on me? I did have a prejudice towards it and her, due to my own ignorance. Furthermore, he had said, that after marriage, I would have to wear *jilbab* as well and I hated him for saying it and so my prejudice just grew.

But the young dentist was pleasant. She wasn't threatening to me at all, and so far no one had looked at me in horror that I wasn't 'dressed' properly. I once went into a shop and I had my niece with me, she was six at the time, and the shopkeeper, whilst taking money from her, quite cleverly told her that she should be covered. Everyone in the shop knew that he was talking about me and I hadn't appreciated it. This was my concern, that this is what the women would say and condemn me. To my surprise, I experienced no hostility of any sort, from anyone. If anything, I was the one harbouring it.

The young dentist started talking to me, and I enjoyed her conversation. Taking her to one side, I sheepishly asked:

'Can you please show me how to wear one of those things?'

For the sake of fitting in, I had gone to the shop and purchased a scarf. I was curious too; I wanted to know what it felt like to wear. Was it that bad? Would people hate me? The talk would begin an hour later and I had no clue as to how to put the scarf on. I didn't want to look a complete idiot and I was nervous standing there. I just wanted to blend in.

'I would be honoured to show you,' she said, and so she did.

At first I thought I would scream and hate it or something along those lines. Surprisingly, nothing happened. But immediately, I felt amazing. When I put it on, it was as if a weight had just been lifted off my shoulders. In some strange way, I felt ... complete. I looked in the mirror and, without blowing my own trumpet, it looked good! I thought it would look awful but just then, that day, I liked what I saw.

The talk began and we huddled into the lecture theatre. I thought I would just hear chants of '*Allah*', but how wrong I was. The speaker, a charismatic lady, talked about a multitude of things, including the rights of animals, purification of the heart, kindness to neighbours, the merits of true sincerity, good deeds, respect for all of mankind irrespective of colour, creed, race, or faith and other differences, death and a range of other things. As I expected, I did hear the word *Allah* and this comforted my heart ... She talked about a man called Muhammad (*sallalahu alayhi wa sallum*), and the more she talked about him, and the way she talked about him and his life, the more my heart wept. Listening to this lady gave me a sense of hope and an incredible sense of empowerment.

As I sat there, I looked around. The lecture theatre was full of intellectual women, some wearing the headscarf and thus 'covered', some not. Women of all ages, from all walks of life; there were academics, professional women, students of various disciplines – Engineering, Law, Dentistry, Mathematics, Physics, Chemistry, English, Botany – you name it, they were there. This was the first time I had seen a different face of Islam. I hadn't been in this sort of circle before. What I had known about Islam was the controlling techniques of *mullahs* [religious leaders, theologians] who insisted that women's place was at home.

'This is where the problem is,' my father would always say. 'The Prophet, *sallalahu alayhi wa sallum*, told us to educate the women, but men have subjugated them and disabled them. By doing that, they are doing the exact opposite to what he taught us.'

I could see it now, it was clear. The interpretation of Islam that my father, an illiterate man, had was the polar opposite to the one being forced on me by Mr Wrong, whose version bore a striking resemblance to the interpretation of Islam that I had run away from as a child: the one heavily rooted in Pakistani culture. Faith and culture are two distinct entities, but somehow they have been enlaced together and the true essence and meaning of the word Islam has been lost along the way.

Growing up in this country, I looked to the Western model of life to compensate for the gap left by my own rejection of some of the stifling traditions of Pakistani culture. However, with the passage of time, I came to know that I didn't belong there either. So, in actual fact, I had always been at a loss.

I was scared, lonely and lost. Walking in the dark, not knowing where I was going, feeling that I had not belonged anywhere. However, for the first time in my life, I felt at ease. Amongst this room of total strangers I mattered, and there was a place for me. I realised that all the colours of mankind, from Africa to Indonesia to India to Canada to Pakistan to Brazil and Albania, we were all connected by one thing: our belief. *Wow* ... this Islam thing wasn't bad. It was supposed to be bad but then why was it making me feel good?

The talk came to an end and we were given the opportunity to ask questions. The questions I wanted answered, however, weren't the ones I wanted to ask in front of everyone. So I waited, just watching the *jilbab*-wearing speaker, fascinated by her intelligence.

My impression of the 'covered woman' changed during the course of that one afternoon, and, as I pondered this, most of the people had now gone. Even though she had been busy with everyone else, she knew that I was waiting for her.

'I don't have much time as we only have this lecture theatre for a fixed period, but I know that you have been waiting for me,' she said as she approached me.

'I don't know who to turn to,' I told her and so I explained my situation briefly.

'Allah has saved you,' she replied.

What?!?? This was someone I 'loved'. How can He have saved me? He has taken something from me, surely He has punished me. But why would He punish me?

'This affliction has befallen you because He wants something better for you. This is not a punishment,' she said. 'There is a *dua* [supplication] that the Prophet (*sallalahu alayhi wa sallam*) taught Umm Salamah when her husband died. The meaning roughly is:

'O Allah! Give me better than what You have taken from me.'

She herself said that she could not imagine anyone better than her husband, yet she said the *dua* when her *iddah* [period of waiting for a divorced/widowed woman, upon completion of which she is then free to marry again if she wishes] was over and she was proposed to by … the Prophet (*sallalahu alayhi wa sallam*) himself. Who could be better than him?!! So try to find solace in this *dua* and trust in your Lord that He diverted something from you that perhaps would not have been good for you. Indeed He is *Al Hakeem* [the All Wise] and *Al Adl* [the Just]. May He who is the Best of Helpers help you.'

She went on to tell me He tests those that He loves the most, the hardest.

'This is a test for you; not a punishment,' she said. 'Your role was to bring two people together, you did that, and you will be rewarded for it, but your destiny is elsewhere. He knows all that which you don't know. You have to accept His decision and put your trust in Him. Know that everything He does, it is for the best. Be patient. He loves those who are patient … *Sabrun Jameel*,' she added.

I recognised that last part; it was from the Qur'an. Yaqub (Jacob), *alayis salaam*, said that when his sons brought him the false news that their stepbrother and Yaqub's most beloved of all sons, Yusuf (Joseph), *alayis salaam*, had been devoured by a wolf. It means 'Patience is beautiful.'

Patience may be beautiful, but how to control the murderous pain of my heart?

'It is in the remembrance of Allah that the heart finds rest,' she said.

I knew that verse too. It was from the thirteenth *Surah*, *Ar-Rad* (The Thunder), *Ayah* [verse] twenty-eight:

*'Allatheena amanoo watatma-innuquloobuhum bithikri Allahi
ala bithikriAllahi tatma-innu alquloobu'*

'Those who believe, and whose hearts find satisfaction in
the remembrance of Allah: for without doubt in the
remembrance of Allah do hearts find satisfaction.'

She gave me her email address and asked me to mail her. As I
left the lecture hall, for some strange reason, I felt different. I
wouldn't say that I was blinded by revelation, but there had
been some sort of awakening. Amongst all that despair lay
relief. I felt as if, from somewhere, there was a ray of light that
was illuminating the path I was walking on. Although still
obscure there was no longer complete and utter darkness.
Now there was a small avenue, visible in the distance. It
seemed inviting and less coarse than the one I was on. My
sore feet felt momentarily soothed ...

As I walked out, I thought to remove the scarf. I had only
worn it as I didn't want to be the odd one out, but now that
the gathering was over, I could go back to normal. I didn't
need the scarf anymore; it had served its purpose so I went to
take it off ... but there was something inside that prevented
me.

So I thought to experiment a little. After all, when would I
ever wear this again? Probably never, and I wanted to know
what it felt like to wear it out there in the big bad world. For
the duration of that afternoon, I had been in the company of
Muslim women, I was one of them, but I wanted to take it to

wider society where I would not be 'one of them' and I wanted to experience what that felt like. So, I started walking.

It felt good surprisingly, not awkward at all like I had imagined it to be. Despite all that bubbling emotion, I felt a shield-like effect coming from somewhere. As I walked to the tube station, I felt proud and it brought about a feeling of elation, that I finally belonged somewhere.

I looked around at people, wanting them to look at me, but no one did. Everyone seemed to carry on with their lives, unaffected by me. I waited to cross the road and an English gentleman driving a van gave way for me. No one else was waiting to cross the road. It was just me; he had stopped for me. He smiled and I smiled back. Thanking him, I crossed the road; quickly, just in case he changed his mind.

It was hot that day, bang in the middle of the summer months. Miraculously though, I didn't feel baking hot as I thought I might whilst wearing the scarf. The only thing was that I wasn't used to the pin under my chin, which was holding it in place and it was uncomfortable at first. I wore it home and as I sat there, for the duration of that train ride, no one looked at me.

By now, I had grown accustomed to the overpowering pain in my heart which came in torrents. The next day, as the agony-drenched memories rushed to my mind like angry waves hitting the shore, I needed to get out of the house. I grabbed my car keys, and then, without even thinking, I reached for the scarf. It was second nature, and I did it without reflecting, hesitating or questioning. I was about to walk out of my door and I thought, '*What are you doing? This wasn't supposed to be a permanent arrangement. You aren't supposed to be wearing this all time. Take it off!*'

I just ignored that voice and went out.

It was awkward in the beginning, as I used to love running my fingers through my hair. I did that a lot and then all of a sudden, I couldn't do that anymore. I resented this at first but, after a while, I completely forgot that I used to love to run my fingers through my hair, after having successfully adjusted my life and my mannerisms to fit around my decision. And that is what it was. It had been my decision to wear it. It was my choice, which is what had been denied to me. The Qur'an states quite clearly in *Surah Baqarah*, the chapter of The Cow (2: 256), that:

> '*La ikraha fee alddeeniqad*'
> 'There is no compulsion in religion.'

Weeks later I went to the *masjid* [mosque] for the first time in my life. I had been overwhelmed by what I had felt at that gathering and I needed to experience it again. I had always been told that only men went to the *masjid* to pray and that the women prayed at home. But as I did my research I found that this couldn't be further from the truth. I liked what I was discovering, from my own curiosity and my exploration of my belief system.

It was as if there was some sort of seal on my heart that had been forced open. Things now started to make sense as I was beginning to uncover a wealth of knowledge. Further enlightenment came from the Ninety-Nine Beautiful Attributes of Allah, and I realised that that is where all my answers lay: with Him. The more I discovered, the more I wanted to know so I began to study the intellectual discipline that is Islam.

Said Muhammad (*sallalahu alayhi wa sallum*):

'For him who seeks a road to knowledge, Allah eases a road to Paradise. The angels lower their wings to him who seeks knowledge, in satisfaction with what he is doing.' [(iv)]

I really did feel as if was getting guidance from somewhere. If anyone reading this can relate to any of what I have said, or for curious folk, my advice is: forget everything that you have ever been taught about Islam. Forget what you see in the media, what you hear from people who are mentally still living in the developing countries. Go back to the first pillar and start from there. Re-educate yourself from scratch as if you are new to the faith, even though you may have been born into this faith. Approach it as if you are just exploring what it is about. Challenge Him, find out Who He is for yourself and see what happens. You might be pleasantly surprised by what you find.

By this stage, I began to feel that although the wound was still there, I had been given some kind of walking aid to help bear the burden of my body. But the heartache persisted. Sometimes, it would be alleviated and a sense of calm would reign. Then sometimes, it felt as if I was reliving the entire nightmare. Of course this was my *jihad* [struggle] – the battle of the positivity of Islam against the negativity of my own self.[9]

> 'The Heavens and Earth cannot contain Me but into the heart of a believer I enter I like a guest.' (v)

Whenever I opened my heart to Him, Allah came to my rescue, but then through my own weakness, I would give in to the constant whispers and find myself back in the same situation. I couldn't stop the self-blame and I hated myself. I kept questioning *why* and *what if*. This was contrary to the advice of the Prophet Muhammad (*sallalahu alayhi wa sallum*) that when something happens, one must accept it as the Decree of God and not try to fight it by 'what ifs', for this allowed *Shaytaan* [Satan] to do his work; i.e. cause despair in the heart of man.

In search of answers, I became a bookworm, roaming the Islamic bookshops up and down the country. As soon as I set

---

9 The earnest personal or physical striving in the way of God; for righteousness and against acts of wrongdoing. Islam distinguishes between:

i. The *jihad asghar* [lesser] defence, fighting to protect Islam from attack or oppression. In such defence, no woman, child or civilian is to be harmed and neither is a tree to be cut down, and
ii. The *jihad akbar* [greater] individual's battle with the '*nafs*' – the soul's lower desires and emotions – against evil and temptation such as lust, greed, envy etc., which serve to corrupt the Muslim, taking him/her away from the remembrance and obedience of God.

foot in the shops, I felt peace; maybe that is why I was attracted to them like a moth to a flame. Whatever it was, it was something, and that feeling precipitated ease, comforting my poor little broken heart.

On one occasion, I had amassed a whole pile of fascinating books: 'Jewels of Guidance;' 'Words that Moved the World;' 'sTime in the Life of a Muslim;' 'Provisions for the Hereafter;' 'Patience and Gratitude;' 'Grief and Depression;' 'Trials and Tribulations;' 'Allah: the Divine Nature,' and as I struggled to carry them over to the till, one particular title caught my eye. Against the idea of purchasing any more books that day, curiously, I turned it over to read the blurb.

It was called 'Don't Be Sad' [vi] and contained advice from the Qur'an and *Sunnah* on how to repel despair and lead a fulfilling Islamic life. There was no way I could leave this book behind. I think it is probably the first book I ever read cover to cover in just one day. I flicked through page after page after page, totally absorbed by what it was telling me . . .

Contemplate and be thankful because the past is no more, what matters is the present. Today is all you have and since you do not know what tomorrow will bring, leave it alone. Just give thanks for what you have, right now, be it little or great.

Deal with bitter criticism in the best of manners, for Allah loves those who conduct their affairs with grace and dignity. Gratitude is not to be expected from anybody for anything, therefore don't be disappointed if your efforts are not appreciated. Do what you do, to seek the pleasure of Allah for your recompense lies with Him and that is what matters and that is where your satisfaction lies.

Do good deeds; excel in charity and kindness for it will comfort your heart and bring you closer to the One who created you, for surely He holds dear those who are charitable.

Counteract boredom and idleness with work, occupy your mind and let not depression or negativity set in. Convert the bitter moments of life into those overflowing with sweetness, for faith and its character is that of optimism and hope. Smile often even and especially when you don't feel like smiling, for it is a great blessing, a charity and charity takes you closer to the Creator, who creates out of nothing.

Your home, however small, is enough for you. As long as you have clothing, shelter and food, you are blessed. Give thanks to Him, even in times of despair and remember the afflicted all around the world compared to whom your suffering amounts to nothing.

The Prayer … the Prayer … don't abandon the prayer, it is your connection with your Creator. It will bring you peace amidst the turmoil. The world's weight is not meant to be carried on your shoulders, so control worry and anxiety so that it doesn't come to control you. Let insignificant things not crush you. Just reflect and give thanks and take not for granted the finer things in life. Appreciate good health and look all around you and you will be the richest of people.

Remind yourself that this life is not yours, it is not your eventuality, nor is it your destination. You are passing through it and the finality is yet to come in the Hereafter.

Pain is a blessing; just reflect. Something harmful can at times be the cause of regaining health.

Learn to control your emotions, let them not run free to destroy you. Keep negativity and boredom at bay.

You have no reason to be sad; your Lord forgives sins and accepts repentance, so turn to Him often. Asking for Allah's forgiveness will open locked doors.

You have no reason to be sad; things happen according to pre-ordainment.

You have no reason to be sad; wait patiently for a happy outcome, for relief is nearby.

You have no reason to be sad; remember the One who created you.

You have no reason to be sad; never give up hope of Allah's mercy, for He is Most Merciful.

Grieve not over criticism from the jealous and the weak-minded. You are above jealousies.

Grieve not over the hurt inflicted upon you by another, and forgive those who ill-treated you, your recompense lies with your Creator. Count your blessings because this is the root of your contentment, so grieve not over unworthy things and overlook the actions of others. This will increase sincerity in your heart and bring you closer to Allah.

Grieve not over the person who forgets and denies the favours you once gave to him, for your desire should be purely for the reward of Allah.

Do not be saddened by fears of what may happen, just trust in Allah, He loves those that trust in Him.

Accept the decisions that fate makes for you and wish not for something you don't have. Appreciate what is allocated to you for that is what Allah has chosen for you, so trust in Him that He has chosen what is best for you.

Let grief not overwhelm you, but instead know the value of the thing over which you feel sad; it is worth so little. Help others, increase in deeds and do good to others and then you will know how worthless your grief is.

In times of distress and despair, remember that forbearance is your only path to both success and happiness. Do not be saddened for the paucity of sustenance for the relief is there, around you, just reflect. With the calamity comes the calm, just be strong you are stronger than you think. Be not shaken by hardship, for you know not how it will end. Be patient. Just be patient.

Spend time alone and reflect. Do you like your own company? Evaluate your personality, if you died today and had to face Allah as you are now, would you be ashamed of who you are as a person? Would your character please Him? Are you true to yourself? Be you, not someone else. He created you to be you not to mimic the personality of another.

There will be other scenes, another life and other days so do not be shaken by hardships. If work piles up, then don't succumb to stress. Do not despair or give up hope when faced with tough situations. The depression will weaken your body and soul. It can be a cause of ulcers and is the road to misery. Do not fall into the traps of depression and anger but rather bear your affairs with serenity.

Happiness is there inside of you; not around you, or outside of you, so seek it.

As long as you have faith in Allah, there is no need for you to be sad. Grieve not over the trivialities of this life for the entire world around you is trivial. Bearing hardships is atonement for sins; Allah is enough for you. Trust in Him.

Confront overt enmity with gentleness for this was the way of Muhammad (*sallalahu alayhi wa sallum*). Look at the righteous and the way they lived their lives. You are not deprived if you have loaf, water and clothes.

Troubles, trials and tribulations are blessings in disguise. Have faith, it is the greatest remedy and will cure all ills. Just believe and be steadfast.

Life is shorter than you think and don't be fooled by what it seemingly holds. Remember you are only here on this earth for an appointed time and you shall take with you only your good deeds for judgement. Make your good deeds plenty for they shall be weighed on a Mighty Day when all shall be held to account.

If you lose a limb, you still have others to compensate for it, so be thankful for you are blessed.

The days will rotate; bringing good and bad, hand in hand, so contemplate on the passage of time for it is fleeting never to return.

Travel through Allah's wide earth; see the blessings and His Marvel. Appreciate the beauty of the universe. And read the signs of the All-Powerful. Explore the cultures, the tribes, the people, the languages, the history and progress of mankind. Seek knowledge! Seek knowledge!

Seek and strive your sustenance without being covetous. Remember, avarice is of no avail. And the fire of enmity will burn you so extinguish it.

Your reality is there and it cannot change, so learn to deal with it.

Do not cling to people in hope other than Allah. Rely on Him and need Him for He will make your path easy and bearable.

Curses and imprecations will not harm you so don't be saddened by those who seek to hurt you.

Don't be angry; alleviate feelings fuelled with anger through supplications and remembrance of Allah. Seek refuge in Allah.

Charity brings peace; it is one of the pillars of Islam. Virtuous deeds are the crown of your faith. So excel in charity, it is an obligation upon you. Take care of your outside as well as your inside. Reflect on this Qur'anic verse: *'And Say [O' Muhammad]: 'Do Good Deeds!'*

Worry not at the delayed sustenance but work hard, for He sees all. Your life is brimming with priceless moments; pause to reflect. Perform beautiful deeds; it is the way to happiness.

Your best companion is a book. By reading books you can develop your talents. Read more, but with introspection and take account of yourself. Knowledge is guidance and cure so write your own history. Read to learn wisdom. Reflect on this Qur'anic verse: '*And when I am ill, it is He Who cures me.*'

Intelligence requires righteousness. Embrace constructive criticism for it will help you improve; always look for ways to attain the best that you can be. Knowledge is the key to serenity and ease, so seek it.

Perform the late-night voluntary prayers when Allah's mercy is at His Greatest, so take advantage of it.

Listen attentively to the words of Allah, He wrongs you not and His Rulings are just. Be thankful when all is well, and He will remember you in times of difficulty. Seek shelter with Allah, He will take care of you.

Your value is superb therefore you have no reason to grieve at poverty. Take advantage of health and free time.

Resentment yields nothing, so keep it at bay. Strive for the fruit of contentment; thankfulness. Dissatisfaction is the door to doubts whereas satisfaction will set your inner self free. Overlook the faults of human beings, it will bring you closer to the Perfect Creator.

Be gentle in your mannerisms, in the way you deal others and the way you view the world.

Be prudent in your everyday affairs and ensure that your intentions are true. Pay attention to your dominant characteristics, you will be judged by them. Be fair in your dealings and avoid being artificial, Allah is pleased with the one whose heart is flowing with sincerity.

Strive for inner beauty; the universe around you will seem more beautiful. Your real wealth is your faith and your character.

Determination can overcome insurmountable barriers so remain positive especially in the face of adversity. Resolve to do something and then do it. The middle course will save you from destruction.

Be gentle with womenfolk, they are your companions and life's treasures.
Allah compensates with better than what is lost, so trust in Him. When something is written to happen, nothing can stop it, so surrender to His Will.

Remember that with the passing of each moment, you draw yourself closer to your ultimate reality; death.
Ponder over this verse of the Qur'an: *The mutual rivalry for piling up of worldly things diverts you (until you visit the graves).'*

Here lay all the answers I needed. It was as if God had taken me by the hand and had addressed each and every single objection, query, doubt and question in my mind.

At that juncture of my life, although the spiritual side of me was beginning to awaken, this was still a slow and gradual process. It couldn't take over and heal me at a rate that I wanted, expected or needed. My heart was shattered to such an extent that it lacked the strength to understand fully. I had various issues to deal with and only in time would it all start to fall into place.

Emotionally I had become an utter wreck, and this gave way to a medical problem. One night, I nearly had a heart attack. It had been inevitable and came as no major shock. For many weeks I had had this tremendous pain as if someone had punched my chest right on my heart.

'When you have your heart broken, especially in this context of marriage or near marriage, it does hurt physically,' Rahila had said. 'It is a physical pain.'

She was right. It was as if I was bruised inside, but unlike any external bruise, which could be treated with ointment and bandages, this was invisible. There was no cure for it, except time itself. Time and prayer were all I had left.

Despite my attempts to spiritually control mind and emotion, I would take two steps forward closely followed by four steps back. Then one forward followed by three back. Psychologically, I was falling apart; physiologically, I was dying a quiet death and mentally, the burden of holding onto a modicum of sanity became a struggle in itself. I began to tread an uneasy path that bordered heavily on insanity.

'You need to talk about it, that is how you will get over it,' Varsha said. 'Talk to us, get it out of your system.'

I think that is the worst thing she could have suggested. Talking about it came to take over my whole life and existence. I managed to void my life of everything else and fixate exclusively on this. Of course, I hadn't familiarised myself with the advice of Muhammad (*sallalahu alayhi wa sallum*), and the verses of the Qur'an which conveyed the idea of 'everything in moderation', in order to stay away from extremism of any sort.

And Varsha hadn't meant it to the extreme that I took it. She meant that bottling things up inside would prove harmful in the long run. So, I talked to as many people as I could, hoping that somehow someone, somewhere could find that button and switch off all the hurt which was consuming my existence. But it was no good; nobody could help me and talking to friends was not working. I needed to talk to a professional.

I asked my GP to refer me to a psychiatrist. I was told it would be months before an appointment would come through, but I was disintegrating fast and he knew this. Luckily, he was able to pull a few strings and I was seen urgently.

I cried so much that day as I drove to the hospital, looking for the Mental Outpatients Department. Is this what my life had been reduced to? Oh how cruel. As I sat there in the waiting room, I saw fellow patients. People out of touch with reality, people who couldn't take care of themselves, people who were perhaps like me once upon a time – normal, sane.

The high-security door opened and along came my psychiatrist. He led me to his office, which was on the other side. He punched in some numbers and swiped a card; the door opened and I followed him. I didn't know whether to cry, lament or be ashamed at my weakness as I walked through that door. I was once full of life, with many dreams. Dreams of love and happiness and ambition and now I was on the brink of madness.

He asked me to explain the situation and I did. He listened. I didn't need him to listen. I didn't need a sympathetic ear. I needed help and he wasn't giving me any. What kind of a professional was he? Why couldn't he just give me an injection or pills or something that would make this vanish? I just needed to forget. Forget it all.

He started scribbling something illegible on my 'file'. And that is when it hit me and I stopped to reflect. All the knowledge that I had accumulated about the One Who created me, this was going directly against all of that.

My Lord had not punished me. He loved me. He was helping me, but I couldn't see because I was blind to His Signs. I didn't need a shrink, or to be locked up in an asylum, and this path of insanity that I had started to walk upon was one that would take me away from Him. This wouldn't bring me success. I would just go on to stumble deeper and deeper in that vortex of my own destruction and end up like my friend Misbah, and this thought scared me.

Misbah had fallen in love with a guy, told her parents and sent them to his house. They went thinking they would finalise the wedding plans, only to find out that the guy was already married and had been for many years. Evidently, he had 'forgotten' to tell her.

The poor girl was so distraught that she spiralled uncontrollably into a state of impassable insanity. For decades now she has been flitting from one asylum room to another, with the odd attempt to integrate back into society and 'everyday life'. Sometimes, momentarily, she is successful and then at other times, she is not and so the pattern continues.

How foolish was I? How ungrateful was I? How undeserving of His Mercy was I? He had blessed me with so much and yet I was so incredibly foolish I couldn't see. The contents of *Don't Be Sad* just flashed in my mind and I realised my error. It was all there. I thought about all the peace in my heart that sometimes would flow like a pure spring deep in the most serene and untouched valley, when I heard the verses of the Qur'an. I thought about the astounding sense of hope that my soul would feel as I prostrated in prayer to the Maker, and the empowerment that my faith was giving me; yet, all of this, I was choosing to ignore. He told me through His Noble Words that:

'La yukallifu Allahu nafsanilla wusAAaha'
'On no soul does Allah place a burden greater than it can bear.'

(*Surah Baqarah*, The Cow 2: 286)

So why wasn't I taking note? Why couldn't I see that:

> *'Fa-inna maAAa alAAusri yusran'*
> 'So, verily, with every difficulty, there is relief.'

> *'Inna maAAa alAAusri yusran'*
> 'Verily, with every difficulty there is relief.'

(*Surah Ash Sharh*, Solace, Consolation, Relief 94: 5–6)

There would be relief from this storm; I just had to be patient. As I sat there, on the fence that divided the rocky path of insanity and the uplifting ray of hope, I realised that He had brought me to that hospital to show me that I was strong and that I had it in me to get my life back on track. In that instant, there was light on my path and it became clear.

The following verse of the Qur'an kept running through my head. Even though I didn't remember it word for word, it had been on the Qur'an tapes that I would listen to and somehow it had become buried in my subconscious mind:

'Allahu nooru alssamawatiwaal-ardi mathalu noorihi kamishkatin
feehamisbahun almisbahu fee zujajatinalzzujajatu kaannaha
kawkabun durriyyunyooqadu min shajaratin mubarakatin
zaytoonatin lasharqiyyatin wala gharbiyyatin yakadu zaytuhayudee-o
walaw lam tamsas-hu narun noorun AAalanoorin yahdee Allahu
linoorihi man yashao wayadribuAllahu al-amthala lilnnasi
waAllahubikulli shay-in AAaleemun'

'Allah is the Light of the heavens and the earth.
The Parable of His Light is as if there were a Niche and
within it a Lamp; the Lamp enclosed in Glass; the glass
as it were a brilliant star; Lit from a blessed Tree, an
Olive, neither of the east nor of the west, whose oil is
well-nigh luminous, though fire scarce touched it; Light
upon Light! Allah doth guide whom He will to His Light;
Allah doth set forth Parables for men: and Allah doth
know all things.'

(*Surah An-Nur*, The Light 24: 35)

'I will book you in for another appointment,' said the
psychiatrist.

But there was no need. I thanked him and, with that, I left.

I drove home, with a barrage of thoughts in my mind. The
reassurance in my heart was that one day I was going to be
fine, because there was something inside me that was strong.
It would be a struggle and I couldn't expect miracles
overnight, but He would help me. I knew He would. He was
the only One who could. He already was; now I needed to
approach Him completely surrendering my heart and soul. I
came home and re-read the *Don't Be Sad* book, and things
started to click into place.

'I am as My servant thinks I am. I am with him when he
makes mention of Me. If he makes mention of Me to
himself, I make mention of him to Myself; and if he makes

mention of Me in an assembly, I make mention of him in an assembly better than it. And if he draws near to Me at arm's length, I draw near to him a fathom's length. And if he comes to Me walking, I go to him at speed.' (vii)

I went to Him, walking, battered, bruised, cut and bleeding, with thorns in my feet, and He healed me (For He is the Best of Healers). I had knocked on His Door, when all other doors closed on me, and He granted me the Mercy of His Protection (For He is the Best of Protectors). When life turned me into a weak bird, lifeless with broken wings, His Guidance would turn me into a phoenix (For He is the Best of Guides).

Time waited for no one, and I had to keep going. The journey was slow but only I could do it. So I kept going.

Eleven: The Show Must Go On

I had to keep going. I was getting sick of the (un)helpful clichés that everyone around me was coming out with:

Plenty of fish in the sea.'
He doesn't know what he has lost.'
You are better out of it.'
If not him, there will be thousands of others.'
Wasn't yours in the first place.'
'Can't argue with God.'
It wasn't meant to be.'

I think out of that little lot, the last one hurt the most. When things aren't meant to be, man is powerless; that is why it hurts more, perhaps?

My exploration of my faith continued as I investigated *marriage*. On spouses, the Qur'an says:

Hunna libasunlakum waantum libasun lahunna'
'They are your garments and you are their garments.'

(*Surah Al Baqarah*, The Cow 2: 187)

I liked that analogy: that the husband and wife were a sacred entity created to complement each other. Shaykh Abdullah Adhami puts it eloquently when he says:

'Just imagine a journey in the winter of Alaska without garments! Our spouses provide us with the same level of comfort, protection, cover, and support in the journey of our lives on this earth as garments would do in the Alaskan journey.'[(viii)]

My research was revealing an entirely different picture of marriage to what I had known and seen in my culture. A woman did not have to do the housework if she didn't want to, and was within her Islamic right to hire help. I looked around me, and the women were slaves in the kitchen and the house. The Prophet Muhammad (*sallalahu alayhi wa sallum*) used to mend his own shoes and do his own chores, whereas most Muslim men, especially the Pakistani ones, are notorious for their machismo and wouldn't be seen dead doing household chores. I am sure things are now changing or have changed, but I am speaking about my own experiences here.

I had always known that *love* before marriage was forbidden, and now I could see why. What was it if nothing but destruction of the self and the soul? Look at me; I was left devastated. The relationship had not received His Blessings and so I had to face the consequences. And despite being disobedient to Him out of His Mercy, He still honoured me through purification. I decided to change my ways and abandon the quest for *love*; a flame that will either warm or burn you. And I certainly did not want to go through what I had done, ever again.

My friend Shanaz, being the relationship expert that she is, said to me:

'You know something? I don't think that *love marriages* work. Everyone I know from university, who ended up having a love marriage, is downright miserable now.'

We would sit there for hours on end, discussing the best modus operandi in our quest to find 'The One'/'Mr Right'/'Mr Half Decent'/'Mister, You Will Do'.

'In my opinion, love comes with time. Look at our parents,' she would say. 'That is love. Staying together, putting up with annoying habits, working hard to pay the bills, worrying about children, creating a decent environment for them, facing old age together and generally dealing with the trials of life, together.'

I knew she was right. I also knew that, so far, I had confused lust with love. I soon came to know that there is a fine line between the two, where one is very much short-lived, leaving behind ruin and despair. However, that did not stop me from wanting romance. My mind was riddled with all sorts of things, and I would be pulled in conflicting directions; between what was right and what I wanted.

In the end I decided that I couldn't deal with more heartache and so going for what was initially right would be the best thing for me. I was also now on a different path and I had to make sacrifices. Besides, the wounds were still sore and I couldn't 'love' anyone ever again. *Marriage is a necessity and love a commodity*, I had always said, and so I would settle this time. I would abandon my quest for passionate love and instead go for companionate love; for the sake of getting married, for the sake of my beliefs, 'for the sake of Allah'.

These words I came to hear when a young 'religious' man replied to me. '*I want to marry you for the sake of Allah,*' he said.

Younger men were now even more unappealing than ever before and, after my experience, I knew that I would not be suited to a younger guy so I turned him down. He wrote back saying how Muhammad (*sallalahu alayhi wa sallum*) was approximately fifteen years younger than his confidante and companion in life, his first wife of twenty-six years, Khadija (may Allah be pleased with her), with whom he had shared a monogamous marriage.

'Age is irrelevant,' he had said. 'What matters is that I fear Allah.'

Emails bounced back and forth before I realised that perhaps I was being unreasonable.

'You can't pick and choose your faith,' he said. 'You have to put your trust in Allah.'

We spoke once and, during the following few days, in our second conversation, he asked me to marry him again.

'Are you crazy?' I asked. 'You don't even know me. You have never seen me or met me and yet you wish to marry me?!'

'You believe in Allah and that is all that matters,' he replied. 'I don't need to see you, I don't want to, I will just send my parents to your house and we can get the vows done and then we can get to know each other.'

He was offering the perfect solution; I did not wish, nor did I have the energy, to fool around with the *let's get to know each other* which was really a shroud so that people could date under the pretence of the *matrimonial* search. It's true isn't it; all these matrimonial websites are 'halal' and 'respectable' just for the sake of culture, religion and social acceptance, when really they are nothing more than the Western model of 'singles' sites?

He said that we shouldn't talk any more if I wasn't going to marry him. I was still in a delicate state of mind and heart, and I thought that it would be easy for me to carry on life, independent of emotion. But completely cutting off my feelings and adhering to the dictates of my head was proving to be difficult. I told him that I couldn't marry him and he hung up.

Days later I heard from him again and he started the same argument. Was this some sort of sign from God? Was I wrong to turn this man down?

'I want to take care of you,' he said. 'It's not right for you to be unmarried when there is a man out there who wants to marry you. I want to take care of you, take care of your heart. Give me your heart.'

Despite my objections, which became weaker and weaker, I caved in, accepting his marriage proposal.

God had answered my prayer. Now I understood what they had all meant when they said that when Allah takes something away from us, He wishes to compensate for it with something better. My new husband-to-be was an established professional like most of his brothers. He was indeed handsome from the photograph on his profile; financially he was secure and intellectually he seemed sound. He would recite the Qur'an to me at night as he had committed it to memory, and in the mornings he would relate *hadith*.

It was crazy and unbelievable at the same time, as we had not even met. Every time we arranged a meeting something always came up at his end. Instead he sent me various photographs. I became worried at this stage. He was like a totally different person in each of them. He tried to tell me that they were taken over the years but I studied the photos carefully.

'Varsha, the features of the face should at least be the same … right?'

'Nasreen, I don't like the sound of him.'

Neither did I, but what could I do? If I didn't marry him, then who else would marry me? The last three years had been testament to that fact; and if that wasn't bad enough, I was fast approaching thirty and no one wanted to marry a thirty-year-old. Varsha knew and understood my predicament and we both agreed that, to a certain extent, people do end up settling. If you didn't, then you had hit the jackpot. Despite her dislike for him, she supported me in my decision, even though it didn't stop her from investigating.

One evening, in between pinning and tacking a pair of trousers, she showed me a printout.

'I don't know how to say this, or what you will think, but I want you to remember that this is only because I care about you,' she said.

'You are beginning to scare me,' I responded, quite terrified, as I didn't know how shocking this news would be and whether my heart could take it.

'He is not who he says he is. He has stolen someone else's identity,' she told me. She then went on to explain how she had tracked down the person who he claimed to be and rang their office. The professional was with a client, whereas 'my suitor' claimed that he was in Bulgaria that week.

'How can that be? How can he be in two different places at the same time?'

If that wasn't bad enough, the address where he claimed he lived didn't exist. But why would he lie? What would he possibly have to gain from this?

'Nasreen, you have got to make him see you. You have to see him in the flesh,' Varsha told me.

Of course she was right. This was as ridiculous as it seemed; I was getting ready to marry someone I had neither seen nor knew anything about.

I confronted him the next time I spoke with him. *Obviously* the secretary had been new and she had mixed up the names of him and his brother. He told me to check on the register, and gave me the link to his certification details. The information checked out. It was as he had said it was.

I checked the residential address and it hadn't shown up on Varsha's search as they were newly built flats which wouldn't appear on the older records. However, when I checked using up-to-date maps, the address did exist.

He went mad that I had listened to a non-Muslim and was taking her word over his. This annoyed me enormously; how dare he? How dare he say this about a person who had cared for me more than any Muslim had ever done? I was trapped and he wanted me to choose between him and my best friend.

'I can't do that,' I told him.

'Well then, we can't be,' he replied.

'That is fine by me.'

When I spoke with Varsha about this she said, 'Nasreen, I would never come between a husband and a wife. If it means that you get yourself sorted and married, then I am happy not to have contact with you after you are married.'

These words shot straight through me. There was no way that I would let her do or say this. She might be happy not being in my life but I refused to share that sentiment.

Days later, he called again, saying he was sorry that he had overreacted. He even tried to make peace by speaking with Varsha on the phone.

When she hung up, she shook her head. 'Nasreen ... he sounds about twelve.'

She was right, he did sound as if his voice hadn't broken yet but you can't have everything I guess. I was just glad that he was from the UK and didn't have a moustache. But this didn't stop doubts in my mind which just gathered momentum by the second. I told him that if he didn't want to meet me, then he could forget it.

'But it is *haraam* [unlawful according to faith] for me to see you,' he said.

His father was an *Imam* [person leading the congregational prayer] and so he wanted to do things properly by leaving it in the hands of the adults. For my own peace of mind though, I needed to know that he did exist. Yes, he would spend hours on the phone to me in the mornings on his way to work, but it wasn't enough.

The next day, he rang to say that he would drop by my house and give me a book to prove that he was real. I waited and a Caucasian female dressed in full Islamic attire, covered head to toe, got out of a car and gave me a package. I couldn't see the driver of the car as they sped off very fast. The female had been his sister-in-law, allegedly.

I had already approached my father about this proposal and he was pleased.

'Dad will not accept the fact that this young man you want to marry has a two-year-old son,' my sister had said.

Once again my father proved her wrong.

'If it does not bother you,' my dad replied, '… then I have no objection. I know that you have a lot of love to give and that you would look after the child as if he was your own.'

I told my dad that he wanted to send his father and his stepmother (his mother had passed away) to see him over the next few days and that we could have the vows done by the weekend after. I knew that my family would have objections to the fact that this had happened quickly and without consulting them, but my father reminded me that I was his daughter and no one else's and, quite frankly, his blessing was all I needed.

I went shopping and must've spent, well, a few hundred pounds on the essentials. My sister and I picked out a wedding dress and he told me not to buy it as he would come with me. That and the gold he said we would buy together. Now, I am

not a great fan of gold and had made my feelings clear that I
didn't want any.

'If it makes you feel any better, I will match the sum of the
bridal dress and the gold and give it to charity,' he promised.

The day came when he was supposed to come to my house
with his dad. Varsha had left work a few hours earlier so that
she could help me with the cleaning, whilst my sister kindly
did the gourmet cooking. This time, only my father and my
sister knew. I didn't want anyone else to know and they
respected my wishes. The plan was that they would arrive at
the *masjid*, pray together and then come home where the food
would be ready.

'How will I know who they are?' my dad had asked.

'He said that they will find you, Dad,' I told him.

So, we waited and waited.

Two hours had gone by and he had neither rung nor sent
me a text me to say that they were late or that they had arrived
at the *masjid*. When I rang him, the phone was switched off,
but I was too ashamed to tell my sister and Varsha, so I told
them that they were delayed.

I went to the kitchen and I overheard my sister and Varsha
talking.

'Do you think this is real?' my sister whispered, without
knowing that I had heard her.

Varsha shook her head. 'I am wondering if all this is a
joke.'

Four hours later, my dad returned. It wasn't a joke; they were just late, that's all. I opened the door and my father walked in. He was alone.

'Dad, where are the guests?' I asked.

Silent, he looked at the floor and smiled. 'They didn't turn up,' he said.

What did he mean they didn't turn up? His father was an *Imam*, of course they would show up. These were God-fearing people, how could they not turn up? It was as if a bulldozer had just flattened me. Letting me down was one thing; I could handle that. Life was beginning to play games with me, so it was ok; but disrespecting my father was something I couldn't stand, nor was I prepared to either.

My father, a gentle elderly man whose compassion was enough to melt even the hardest of hearts, had sat there in the *masjid*, despite his arthritis, with his eye on the entrance, waiting for a young man and an elderly father to walk through. And he had done this for four hours. In the end, his knees couldn't handle it anymore and he had given up and asked someone to drop him off home.

I sent a text to say that God-fearing people had the decency to let someone know if they had no intention of turning up and that I would not forgive him for what he had done to my father.

He sent the following text message to my phone:

'La'aabudu ma ta'aabudoona
Wala antum AAabidoona maaAAbudu
Wala ana 'aabidun ma'aabadtum

Wala antum AAabidoona maaAAbudu
Lakum deenukum waliya deeni'

I was deeply shocked. I knew this verse; it was from the
Qur'an, *Surah Kafirun*, The Disbelievers, 109: 2–6, and it is
translated like this:

'I worship not that which ye worship,
Nor will ye worship that which I worship.
And I will not worship that which ye worship,
Nor will ye worship that which I worship
To you be your way, and to me mine.'

I couldn't understand what was going on; nor could I tell
anyone what had just happened. How could I? Instead I put
on a brave face and told my sister and Varsha that something
had come up and that they couldn't make it. So, we put the
dishes away and were left eating the food for days to come.
We never talked about this again in our house.

He rang me for a long time after that; telling me that he
was sorry. But sorry just wasn't good enough. I had
compromised too much and I wasn't willing to any more.

'Just leave me alone please,' I told him one night.

'Why?' he had the nerve to ask.

'Because you are a liar, and I have no time for liars. Just
remember who is watching you. He knows everything that you
do and have done. Don't ever call me again. For the sake of
Allah, please leave me alone.'

I went to the cemetery where he said his mother and brother were buried. Near that bench, by that tree; there were no graves there. I searched the whole of that cemetery for headstones bearing their names. I found nothing. Apparently, they had died many years earlier. He had said *'Wa'Allahi'* [I swear by Allah's Blessed Name] that they are buried there … *'Wa'Allahi'* was his favourite phrase and he used to say it with almost every word he uttered.

Once again, Allah, the Most Glorious, the Supreme, out of His *Hikmah* [Wisdom] taught me an invaluable lesson. We sometimes judge people and assume that those who 'appear' religious are better believers than those who do not. This proved otherwise. This proved that it is not necessarily the case that anyone who praises and remembers Him day and night is a good person. Sincerity lies in the heart and to that no one has access except the One who does:

'Waasirroo qawlakum awi ijharoo bihi innahuAAaleemun bithati alssudoori'

'And whether you hide your word or make it known, He certainly has (full) knowledge of the secrets of (all) hearts.'

'Ala yaAAlamu man khalaqa wahuwa allateefualkhabeeru'

'Should He not know – He who created? And He is the
One that understands the finest mysteries (and) is well
acquainted (with them).'

(*Surah Al-Mulk*, The Sovereignty, Control 67: 13–14)

This would also show me that there was no place in this
cruel world for me, and that I needed to keep striving towards
Him. When He wants good for us, He subjects us to hardship
and this encounter just served to strengthen my resolve. I sat
there in the solitude of my room, in the depths of that night,
surrounded by a mélange of emptiness and loneliness, but I
knew that in my life lay many trials compared to which this
would be insignificant and that He would bring to me better
than He took away from me. So I had to remain strong.

Varsha and I never discussed this again. I think she felt my
embarrassment and so out of the goodness of her heart did
not wish to embarrass me further. So we pretended that this
did not happen. Years on, when I would come to write this
chapter, she finally let her feelings be known:

'I think I hated him the most out of all your experiences.
Why? Because you were at your most vulnerable(est), ok,
linguist deal with that. [I am sitting my final exam on
Thursday, can't wait to get over this course, but at least I
now know what prepositions and articles are and finally
can understand your jokes without having to reach for the
dictionary.] I hated him and deep down, which I never

shared with you, thought someone put him up to his little sick game.'

But whatever was/was not, I know that my justice lies with the One Who saw all, and heard all, and knew all. He knew what was in my heart then; He knows what is in my heart now; and He knows what shall come to be in my heart. Therefore, I am content.

Spiritually I refused to let this break me. There was no reason that it should. Emotionally, however, the final scene of a movie that I had studied at university kept playing continuously in my head.

Calle Mayor (1956), a prominent Spanish auteur film, directed by Juan Antonio Bardem, is the story of a group of provincial louts who play a cruel joke on a local spinster. One of them, Juan, pretends to fall in love with her, but while she is busy making final arrangements for the wedding, he jilts her as he had no intention of marrying her in the first place. The movie closes with her left by her window, watching the rain as it pours down the glass, and we, the viewers, see the tears which are pouring down her face.

'*Isabel, ¿No tienes novio?* ' [Isabel, you don't have a boyfriend do you?] had been the strapline around which that movie is based. And certainly it is central to a key scene where Isabel tells Juan that it first had been her girlfriends, all married or engaged, who had chorused that question out of malicious spite; then her aunts who compared Isabel to their own married daughters; then her own mother who was worried by the financial consequences of Isabel's spinsterhood until eventually, Isabel, shortly before she meets Juan, arrives at the conclusion that she was a failure and that no one wanted to marry her.

I stopped searching for someone after this horrible incident and spent the next six months trying to come to terms with my life and the state that it was in. The show had to go on, yes, but I needed a break. I realised that I didn't need to be searching for someone, but for my own self. So the curtain came down. For a while.

Twelve: Where There's a Will, There's a Way

During my 'sabbatical', periodically Shanaz would ask if I wanted to get back to the whole matrimonial scene. She felt that I needed to look to the future, and start the next chapters of my life. But I was fed up. I was sick of the whole routine, the politics; the bureaucracy that it all entailed. It terrified me too that I might actually find someone. I didn't want to go through the whole process again. Twice I had involved my family and I didn't want to risk it again.

'But things have changed. We don't have to go down the Internet route,' she would say. 'There are all sorts of other options now.'

She was right. When I started looking, the online matrimonial business was still a fledgling endeavour. You could count on one hand the few websites that existed. Gradually though, the concept of 'speed-dating' entered the arena, being welcomed and accepted by many. In addition, *padlock and key parties* were increasingly all the rage alongside dinner events, boat parties and the newly formed '*Social Groups*' – like-minded individuals getting together on a regular basis to participate in social activities, such as picnics, trips to the theatre, holidays abroad and such like. So I returned to find that during my absence, the whole face of the partner search had been radically transformed.

For those who are still going through the pain of *looking*, or have been through it, you will no doubt agree that at some

point you find yourself highly demotivated. You will ask
yourself if you can be bothered or whether this is all that is left
for you. You may even take a break but the thought of being
shipped off to your parents' country of origin is enough to
bring you back to the endless charade of trying to find
someone. Whichever applies to you, you will have at some
point questioned the reliability of the Internet.

Having had enough of the 'no result' of cyberspace, at
one point I suggested to Shanaz that we broaden our nets and
try different waters; perhaps a dinner event.

'You are joking, right? I don't think I can handle a whole
evening stuck with someone I don't like looks wise,' was her
response.

In the end, I abandoned the dinner idea. Going to the
cinema alone was bad enough but having to turn up at these
events with just me, myself and I was something with which I
really couldn't cope. I was not about to go on my own,
declaring to the world that I was single and not wanting to be.
Besides, I had already had some sort of experience with the
'dinner' route that I wasn't prepared to repeat at any cost.

Varsha once took me to a birthday gathering of a close friend
of hers. I had been told that I was needed for *moral support*.
When we got there, it became evident that she would have had
plenty of moral support even if I had not accompanied her.

'I may have forgotten to mention that Jamaal has invited a
few eligible bachelors,' she whispered in my ear as we arrived
at the restaurant. I think that was an understatement. When we
got there, the Jamaal party was full of single brown females,

under thirty, with the other side of the table being occupied by a handful of eligible bachelors. It was official – the birthday party had now been hijacked by desperately seeking single folk.

This was the least of my worries though. As soon as we had walked in and before she had confessed, I had my suspicions from the way that a certain young man had looked at me. I didn't appreciate him staring, almost piercing me with his eyes. I was tempted to go over and slap him but I got the impression he would have enjoyed that too much.

We sat down and exchanged pleasantries with the other guests. There was one bachelor who was rather alluring; an opinion obviously shared by many of the females on that table.

'I already asked about him,' Varsha whispered. 'He is engaged.'

Oh blast! … But then isn't that the way; the ones that you are interested in are always unattainable?

We carried on enjoying the ambience, listening to the views of the others as a battle of minds, intellect and social class was already in full swing. My potential suitor, whose box I had ticked as soon as I had set foot in the restaurant, was a barrister and had no problem voicing his Tory opinions on affairs of the Middle East (although now he probably votes Labour, since there is no longer a difference between the two). Approaching our end of the table, thinking that by now I was fully impressed with him, he asked, 'So what do you do for a living?'

'Hello, I am very well thank you. And how are you?' was my response.

Why do people do that?!?? *Why* is occupation of such pressing nature? Surely there are other things one can say to break the ice? We were, after all, in a fine restaurant; could he not have commented on the food or the atmosphere or even introduced himself in a more appropriate manner rather than the way he approached us?

I looked at Varsha, and Varsha looked at me, and we looked at Isma, and then Varsha replied,

'Well actually, I am unemployed and so is she, and so is she.'

Mr *Barrister-Sans-Humour* then walked off.

We had been appalled by the behaviour of some of the people at that table. Isma and her husband didn't quite fit into the category of investment bankers, lawyers or economists who happened to be at the dinner and it had made them feel out of place and awkward. I was quite disgusted by the way some of those individuals had chosen to ignore the fact that they were sitting there too. And of course since the barrister had made it clear that he was interested in me, some of the females, who were perhaps hoping to trap him, decided that they would ignore me too. This was fine by me. Varsha, Isma, Tehmoor (Isma's husband) and I spent that evening enjoying each other's company without participating in the, *Who is better? / Which car do you drive?* competition.

Days later Varsha passed on a message that the barrister had been interested and wanted to meet me again. I had a feeling as soon as we had walked into the restaurant that that would be the case. Maybe his whisper in Jamaal's forty-two-year-old ear gave me a clue, or maybe Jamaal's forty-two-year-old hand motioning the '*leave it with me I'll take care of it*' action gave it away?

'I know what your response is, but I said that I would pass on the message,' Varsha said.

I did appreciate her keeping her word but seriously, he really was not the kind of guy I was interested in. Having observed his behaviour that evening, his idea of passion would be reading the law reports to me in bed. Furthermore, I neither appreciated nor welcomed the way that he had managed to pick me out as soon as I stepped into the restaurant. It couldn't have been my delightful personality that had won him over, surely?

'*Looks*' was again the central component with the dinner route. It was all about physical appearance. I might as well have just turned up at a Pakistani wedding, sat next to the bride and then waited for parents of eligible bachelors to 'make enquires' about whose daughter I was.

So the dinner thing was out.
My extraordinary guy would not be at some dinner …

'Nasreen, I think we should go speed-dating,' Shanaz said one evening.

I don't know if that was more for my benefit or hers, but it was something that did not interest me. The whole process of finding someone online is artificial as it is, but for me, the way that a person communicates on a written level is highly important. Shanaz, however, is the opposite.

'I don't like to mess around when looks are everything to me,' she admits openly.

There is nothing wrong in admitting that or for even wanting looks to be at the top of the list. As I have said throughout this book, it is very much dependent on what you are seeking in a partner and what works for one person is unlikely to work for another. To me, speed dating was just like a meat market, where everyone would be immaculately presented, on their best behaviour, only talking to you if they liked the look of you. As I have continuously stressed, I didn't want something based on looks and looks alone.

Let me share something with you. My cousin went to one of these events recently, and there he saw a most beautiful woman. She was wearing the headscarf and dressed in the full *jilbab*. Now this cousin is unreceptive to either of these items of clothing, the latter even more so, yet he was totally captivated by this lady and didn't care how she was dressed (let that be a lesson to men out there who think that a woman who observes *hijab* is unattractive). He didn't care about her personality or values, but was only concerned with what she looked like.

The thought of meeting forty people in one evening and picking those that you are attracted to seems to be a fantastic idea. But again, this would be something that would not work for me. What are the statistics of people making their minds up about you within the first few seconds that they see you? … So I figured that seeing me with a scarf would be enough to have men running for the hills. One professional young man I once was 'chatting to' on the instant messenger logged off as soon as I mentioned that I wear the scarf. He didn't even say goodbye. Prior to my revelation, we were having a great conversation.

The way I saw it, it didn't matter how bubbly my personality may be (although come and find me at a certain time of the month and you will quickly change your mind) or how great my character is, people would have their preconceived notions about who I am and treat me accordingly, with a complete disregard to who I actually am, which may be the exact opposite to who they think I am or may want me to be!

Many years ago a friend went to a speed-dating event.

'They gave us three minutes each but even thirty seconds were too much for me.'

'Why is that, Tariq?'

'Well the first question I was asked was, *what was your degree in?* and the second question the women asked was, *where in Pakistan are you from?*'

Tariq didn't have a degree and his parents were from Mirpur.

'You should've seen the look of, *not interested in you!* ' he said to me.

Feedback from a female perspective was more or less the same. Nazish, a friend of mine, told me that it was a total waste of time. Most men hadn't been attracted to her, and rather than be polite for the duration of those three minutes, they were rude and made it obvious that they didn't like what they saw.

So when Shanaz suggested going speed-dating, I imagined myself sitting there and going through the same script over and over and over again, that, *'Yes, I observe hijab and no, it wasn't a reason to be put off, that yes, I was still a human being inside, that no, I was no different to those women who were sitting beside me, and that yes, I still had the same desires and feelings that they did.'* I was sick of having to justify myself, my existence and my decision, to almost every prospective husband that I was beginning to come across.

So the speed-dating thing was out.
My extraordinary guy would not be speed-dating ...

Not too long ago, I went to a 'networking' event. I thought I was going to 'network' but when I got there I discovered that it was a *singles* event. I think more and more people are beginning to acknowledge that the Internet is a waste of time and so other avenues are being explored. I asked the organiser if it had been a singles event all along, to which she replied 'no'. Of course one major problem was that most of the women there were 'single', 'thirty-plus' and 'looking'. Unfortunately, to our horror, the men were few and far between. I recognised one of the women there. She was a friend of a friend of mine and when I first starting looking five years ago, I heard of the plight of this woman and how much of a problem she was having trying to find someone and settle down because of the fact that she was in her mid-thirties.

'I hope that that doesn't happen to me,' I had thought to myself. I am now fast approaching the age that she was, way back then.

Even more alarming is the fact that it is the same people who turn up to these events. Whilst networking, I heard many say that it was the exact same people who had turned up to another event organised by a different company. I have just received details of another scheduled event; I can already guess who will be there!

So the networking thing was out.
My extraordinary guy would not be networking ...

Waves have also been made in those traditional *Aunty-ji*[10] circles. Not too long ago, I came across an advert in the newspaper about a professional matchmaker: an Aunty who 'guaranteed results'. This should be good news for all those parents who object to or are uncomfortable with their offspring resorting to the World Wide Web on their own.

Even though this particular entrepreneurial Aunty has her own website, I am sure that parents would forgive her because, in their eyes, it is still the 'respectable' thing to do: to go through the elders. Traditionally, all mothers knew someone who knew someone who knew the 'lady who helped with *rishtey*' [marriage proposals]. This lady, the 'Pakistani Cupid' (but without the whole love thing, of course!), would

---

10 '*ji*' is a suffix used as a mark of respect.

know exactly whose daughter needed marrying and who had a
son that might be interested in that girl of *marryable* age. I
wasn't even aware that these matchmaking women existed in
the UK until years ago when Shanaz pointed out that the
Aunty of a friend of hers arranged introductions.

'Shall I sort something out for you?'

'No thank you,' I replied.

I really did not need some interfering woman displaying me
and showing me a string of useless and unsuitable men.
Besides, I knew that my extraordinary guy would have nothing
to do with the Aunty route, because he would have better taste
than that!

So the Aunty route was out.

My extraordinary guy would be undetectable by the Aunty
radar ...

In my opinion, this Aunty route was more for mothers who
refuse to give their offspring autonomy in searching for a
partner. Certainly, some people prefer to let their parents do
the hard work. Someone I know says he wants nothing to do
with the search and has instructed his parents to find him a
suitable girl. Whoever they pick, he will gladly accept. Whilst
you cannot help but admire the respect and trust that he has
placed in one of life's greatest blessings, i.e. parents, the guy
evidently has a screw loose.

Then there are those British Pakistanis, be they male or
female, who are limited by the somewhat unfortunate cultural
restraints of their parents. I am extremely lucky in the sense

that I do not have set criteria imposed upon me regarding my choice of marriage partner. Sadly I know many people who have been given stringent checklists by their family, to which they must adhere when considering bringing home, for parental approval, a potential spouse.

'Caste' always seems to top most lists. Despite claiming to be Muslims, it is amazing how many parents are bound by it, due to its cultural significance in traditional Pakistani life.

I once spoke with someone who, within the first five minutes, asked me, 'What caste are you?'

'I am Muslim,' I replied

'Yes, of course, but what caste?' he repeated.

'Well ... you see if I was from a faith which has its foundations in the caste system, then I could answer your question but sadly, as a Muslim, I am not concerned with something that my faith does not recognise.'

He was a pleasant young man but unfortunately my values and his, or rather those of this family, would be unable to co-exist. In all fairness, there are hundreds of second-generation British Pakistani Muslims who are not bothered with this issue of whether someone is a *Raja* or a *Choudary* (near the top end of the social scale) or a carpenter or chef (nearer to the bottom of the league) but who, for the sake of their parents, feel the need to comply and can only marry someone who is of '*equal*' status. Of course, there are those who, despite being professional and educated, prefer to comply with tradition out of their own free will. It is very much a personal thing.

Me? I am happy with the values of my belief system: that all of the colours of mankind are equal and that subsequently

kings, peasants, young, old, surgeons and shoemakers will all
be wrapped in a single white shroud and buried in exactly the
same way. Nothing more. Nothing less.

While we are on the subject of what is acceptable in faith,
as mentioned earlier, there is a strong element of 'cyber dating'
when it comes to this online matrimonial route. Despite the
attempts to keep things halal, I sometimes wonder if it can
ever really be halal? I know now of a dinner event service
which lays down strict guidelines of a number of meetings but
even then, in my personal opinion, this can never fully be
strictly adhering to Islamic etiquette.

I tried a *halal as possible* marriage event. We were given
specific instructions not to violate the Islamic guidelines that
had been set out by the organisers: namely that the partici-
pants were not allowed to have direct contact with each other
before, during or after the proceedings and that any
communication was to be via the facilitators. When the event
started, we were huddled into the hall which was separated by
a large screen in the middle. The profiles were displayed at the
back of the hall, with the male ones on the female side and the
female ones on the male side. If you were interested in a
profile, you had to speak with the facilitator who would then
speak with his wife, or, if female, then the facilitator would
speak with her husband who was also a facilitator and then
communication would take place through them. *Valis*
[parents/guardians] were encouraged to attend the event and I
did feel slightly odd turning up alone. I found it embarrassing
to drag my father or brother or sister to an event where we

would be shopping for a potential husband. So I left them at home.

Whereas I appreciated and respected the fact that these organisers had tried to adhere to correct protocol, I felt that since the majority of people who attended that event were not 'practising', this method would be a complete waste of time for them. I watched the mothers from both sides as they scoured the hall in search of the most attractive looking matches for their offspring. It was at that moment that I walked out.

So the halal events were out.

My extraordinary guy would not be at a halal event ...

After agreeing that the Internet approach was not working, Varsha decided it was time to take matters into her own hands and use the *'personal acquaintance'* route.

She mentioned to her friend Isma (from the uncomfortable dinner with Mr *No Humour Barrister*) that I was single (i.e. desperate) and asked whether she knew of anyone suitable. Subsequently, I was roped into a meeting *chez Isma*.

When we got there the eligible bachelor had yet to arrive. I was glad. I had been totally against the idea right from the start but, out of respect to Varsha and the fact that she had gone to so much trouble for me, as well as Isma who had invited me to her home and cooked for us, I felt that the least I could do was turn up, smile and be pleasant. Deep down though, I cringed.

Varsha knew this. Actually, she is great. She most definitely has an extra sense. Everyone has five but she has six. Seven even. No, I take that back. Considering she is so sharp, she has eight.

'What is your problem?' she asked me as we drove to Isma's house.

I explained how desperate I must have appeared to Isma and Tehmur that no one wanted to marry me, and now I was on my way to their house to meet a potential husband. They probably wondered why I was single, as almost everyone I came across eventually asked me that horrid question.

Since Tehmur and 'my date' were extremely delayed, we decided to have dinner without them. Apparently, there had been some sort of problem at the shop, but I think we all knew that they were just on Pakistani time. I was so relieved though. At least I wouldn't have to go through the humiliation. Our evening came to a close and as we got up to leave ... they arrived. Why couldn't the earth just have swallowed me whole?

He kept staring at me and as much as I tried to hide the fact that I was dying quietly, I don't think it took a genius to figure that one out. I was not impressed; nor was Varsha. It wasn't the poor guy's fault though; the situation wasn't right and I knew it and so did everyone else in that room. We left politely making a sharp as possible exit. I felt bad that we didn't stay for coffee but, as Varsha said, *'If I didn't get you out of there when I did, you would have hyperventilated!'*

So the friends route was out.

My extraordinary guy would not be the friend of a friend ...

Undeniably, the partner search hits all sorts of plateaus, often forcing you to think the unthinkable. I had a friend who called me up to announce that although I would not like the decision that she had made, she felt that there was no other way for her.

'My parents have found someone who is here on a student visa. He is ok. I know it's not what we would ideally want, but once you are married, none of these things matter,' she said.

Another friend had said that she was ashamed to be 'scraping the barrel' by resorting to some matrimonial service a Pakistani television channel was running.

My own sister even told me that our eldest brother wanted to know what I had decided about my future and if it was necessary for him to start searching for someone ... from Pakistan.

'He will be the way you want him to be,' she said. 'It might not be that bad, you know. I did it and look how happy I am.'

I replied with an expletive.

So, the abroad route was out.

My extraordinary guy would not be abroad ...

Out of all these avenues I think I still prefer the online route even though it is quite an expedition and you are often subjected to the same trials as you would be when you are looking for a job. In fact many parallels can be drawn between trying to find a partner and trying to find employment. The CV like a matrimonial profile is a marketing tool. Ultimately, it is selling 'you'. One person even wrote as the opening line to his profile, *'Here is the CV!!'* And then of course you get comments like 'such and such people need not apply'. That always makes me laugh: the idea of 'applying'. I once said to Varsha that I had seen a very nice profile and that I had 'applied' to be his wife. Sadly, I was unsuccessful in my application as he did not acknowledge my response, just like many rude employers out there who never get back to you. I mean how many times have you sat there, carefully writing targeted covering letters and CV's, only to receive no reply at all? It's awful, I know.

Mind you, sometimes friends and family 'sift' suitable candidates and so you never really stand a chance in the first place. I have lost count of the number of times I have read profiles with, *'I am writing this on behalf of a friend.'* This always makes me curious; is this really true, or did the person write their own profile but were too embarrassed to be looking on the Internet and so didn't want to admit that?

When it comes from parents though, there is no element of doubt that you will have to undergo a strict selection procedure.

'We (my husband and I) are from Pakistan. Our son was born in Holland and grew up in America, where we now live. After initial contact with us (parents), you would be corresponding with our son. Let us know if interested. Parents'

This had been a reply I received from parents who had stated in their son's profile that they specifically sought:

'A well-educated daughter-in-law (country of origin immaterial) preferably lady doctor, engineer, physical sciences or other higher education, slim to medium built, of fair complexion.'

I replied:

Dear Parents,

Thank you very much for getting in touch with me. However I feel that I do not fit your category of wants in a prospective daughter-in-law. I am no lady doctor, nor engineer, nor do I have any association with the sciences, physical or other. I am just an ordinary girl.

I look forward to hearing from you.

Kind regards,
Nasreen

The parents never did reply back.

Siblings also have our best interests at heart. One young man told me that his brother had decided to take charge of the search. Out of all the responses he had sifted through, he had been most impressed with me.

'Who is actually the one seeking marriage?' I asked.

'I am,' he replied.

And look there you go, the idea of sifting through, doesn't it bear a striking resemblance to being 'shortlisted' for the next stage? In the first example above, I was unsuccessful with the parents, and in the second, I passed to the next round and was invited for interview, or in matrimonial terms, 'Let's meet for coffee.'

Coffee … What a nightmare that is. The amount of coffee I have had to drink during the course of my search is phenomenal. I am surprised that I have not turned into a coffee bean. The sad thing is that I don't even like coffee. Besides, when you meet for coffee, do you ever really meet *just* for coffee? As in an interview situation, aren't you under close scrutiny? The way you are dressed, the way you look, the way you sit there, your body language in general, the conversation as a whole; everything. Doesn't coffee determine whether you see that person again?

If you do, then congratulations! You have made it through to the next stage. Maybe this involves another coffee or perhaps the more rigorous psychometric testing of *going for a meal?* I don't know. I was never lucky enough to be invited to second-stage interviews.

After that comes the assessment centre of meeting friends. This is a crucial aspect of the whole application. Should you pass this, you might go on to the final selection procedures of the panel interview, where parents and family take it upon themselves to ascertain if you will be good enough for their son/daughter/sister/brother.

If you are lucky enough to pass these hurdles, you may be offered a permanent role. If you take up the position, you will be required to sign a binding contract, otherwise known as the marriage vows. Sounds straightforward, but it is far from that. There are many obstacles along the way.

Allow me to tell you about some of them.

Thirteen: Money Talks

One of my great litmus tests was to see if any guy would ask me to ring him back. As soon as I would hear, '*Which network are you on?*' or '*Do you have free minutes because this is costing me,*' I would know instantly that the guy was not for me. There was even one time when, after having exchanged numbers with someone, my phone rang then stopped after a few rings. I called back and we spoke. Days later he rang again and the same thing happened. His missed call, it seems, was a signal for me to call him back. I didn't bother with him after that.

I understand fully and appreciate that money is not something to be wasted, but penny-pinchers are a major no-no. I don't have an extravagant lifestyle but I could not live with a man who would want change back with a receipt. I have never done that in my life. My father was always generous with money and he would be insulted whenever I gave him change. Yes, it's true – women look for traits of their father in the man that they marry!

Another experience that I am unlikely to forget in a hurry was when I met someone who had been as disappointed in me as I had been in him. My disappointment however would turn out to be rather more expensive than his. After the coffee-filled pleasantries he suddenly went to the *boys' room* to powder his nose.

When the waitress came up to me for the second time asking if we wanted to order anything else, I took that as a cue to vacate the café. They were turning customers away and needed our table. By now, it was obvious that my potential husband had drowned in the toilet so I should pay and go. As soon as I had paid, lo and behold … he came out from nowhere.

'You can come out now, I have paid the bill,' I said as I got my things.

He did not even bother to apologise for running off, nor did he thank me for doing what he should have done, nor did he offer to reimburse me, not that I expected, nor wanted him to. It was the principle at stake. Needless to say, we never contacted each other again. Even if he had tried, we wouldn't have got far. As we sat there for the brief time that we did, he spent most of it trying to guess how much everyone around us earned. I am so glad that I didn't end up marrying him; there would always have been three of us in the relationship: me, him and the calculator.

Another time, I met someone in a slightly upmarket Central London postcode. It worked out for us both as I got to spend a few hours in the exclusive shops and he didn't have to travel far to meet me. In fact all he had to do was open the door of his flat, go down the stairs, open another door, cross the road and walk into the café. I think his journey to meet me took him all of two minutes.

This eligible bachelor seemed glad to see me. His head hadn't revolved and fallen off, and no smoke came out of his ears. Neither of us knew what the other looked like. As always,

I didn't really care, so I hadn't asked for a photograph. Neither had he.

It was a summer's evening and he had that *Miami Vice* dress sense. I liked that. Before we ordered the coffee (mine was mineral water, of course), he apologised that he had locked himself out of his flat and therefore didn't have his wallet. Oh poor thing!

'What will you do?'

'It's ok, I will just call the locksmith out,' he replied. 'Luckily, I've still got my mobile!'

We talked, enjoyed each other's company and when it was time to leave, I picked up the tab. It was not a problem. He kept asking me when he would see me again. Deep down I think I knew that although he seemed okay enough, somehow it didn't feel right. He wanted a relationship of some sort, most likely physical, as he had made clear and, unfortunately, I would have to go home and clock in and out so it wouldn't work. He kept insisting that we meet again and that we set a date for the next meeting. I managed to wriggle my way out and promised to email him and that we would certainly speak again. I did mail him the following day, but he didn't reply back. Surprised at his behaviour, and how keen he had been, I was disappointed too. It was my own fault; why didn't I just set a date for our next meeting? I can be so dumb sometimes. But I did learn a valuable lesson – Never leave home without your purse because if the guy accidentally forgets his wallet, then there will be a problem.

Of course, the opposite end of the money scale is just as bad. I spoke with someone who, during the first conversation, told me he worked in Park Lane and lived in an affluent part of London. The second time we spoke, he told me about his recent stay at the Hilton. Upon the third conversation, he told me about how he was going away on a long holiday, one month to the Seychelles. The fourth time we spoke, it was the fact that he had just bought a car, but that he was going to get a Porsche as his 'weekend' car. I didn't pursue anything with him in the end. I felt that he would say these things just to impress me.

His talk of what he had really put me off. Rather than attracting me, it had the opposite effect. He was not to know my feelings about money and I didn't make an effort to explain it to him. Right from the moment that I set out on this search, I decided that I would not enter into a marriage without a pre-nuptial agreement (which I now find that the English courts do not recognise; how silly of them). In my life, I have always had everything that I ever wanted. My father provided for us, more than we ever expected or dreamed of, and I am not hungry for money. As an adult, I saw what money did to people around me and I didn't like it and I certainly didn't want a man for his money; I have enough of my own. No one knows what is ever around the next corner or indeed what fate has in store for us in the long run; but should I ever leave a marriage then I would not want to take anything with me that wasn't mine.

Besides, money can be replaced. I will not.

Fourteen: Losers, Playboys & Slick Pythons

As in real life, cyberspace is almost certainly brimming with sub-varieties of the above. I know; I came across plenty. I am sure that if we were to collect stories from people there would be a whole anthology of 'unbelievable yet true' revelations. Of course I do not insinuate that only men are guilty; women can be just as bad.

Tariq once told me of his experience which left me slightly shocked. One afternoon he called me to take a look at a website. I did, and I found a message on a girl's profile, saying that Allah had given her a man and that she couldn't believe that she had *'resorted to a sad site full of useless t*ssers who couldn't get a woman'*. A few weeks later, the same girl rang him up as they had spoken shortly before she had found her dream man and left the message. She asked if he wanted to pursue communication with her. It turned out that her boyfriend had dumped her and she had been on the rebound when she put up her original matrimonial advert. When he had come back to her, she left the nasty message because she no longer needed to be on the site. However, since he had dumped her again, she was available once more. She was reminded aptly by my friend that he was just another one of the sad useless t*ssers to which she had referred, and that he was *'looking for a wife not a b*tch'*.

Losers

The (cyber) world is a very small place. People come to know one another and everyone gets to find out about others' business. *'Let's be friends'* leads to horrific encounters being shared and it spreads from there. What doesn't help is having a bulletin board or discussion page on a website. Like one guy, for example, soon came to discover.

One day, we all awoke to find that a new female member had left a message exposing a certain young man. This poor girl was left very hurt by him and, as you can imagine, she was bitter. By lunchtime, there was a whole string of messages from other women who had said what a complete loser and time waster he was as they too had met him.

Apparently, he was bad at telling women that he wasn't interested and instead preferred to keep them hanging with false promises that he would tell his parents and that they would be coming to their house. I also had the pleasure of meeting him once and had decided not to pursue or keep in contact as he had suggested.

'Why not?' he asked.

'Because, my friend, you are really not the man for me.'

'But I have green eyes,' he said.

'And I have hazel ones,' I replied.

Bless him. I think he thought that I would be won over by the golden carrot of his green eyes. It was not his fault; in the Pakistani community if your eye colour is different from the usual black/dark brown, then you are a great catch.

And then once I went to meet a prospective who obviously didn't like the look of me because as soon as I got out of the car, he suddenly started to dial his phone. Nodding as if to say '*Hi*', he then mouthed that he was, '*Sorry, but needed to attend to this phone call*'.

'It's ok, please go ahead,' I said.

I waited.

And I waited

And I waited.

Nearly twenty minutes had gone by and he wasn't getting off the phone. So I got up, grabbed my bag and headed for my car.

He quickly got off the phone and shouted, 'Wait, you can't do this!'

'Who says I can't?' I asked as I reversed my car.

I felt bad that I had been rude, driving off like that. But then I hoped that he felt equally bad for the disrespect he had shown me.

Another potential suitor seemed normal until we started talking about our parents' origin from Pakistan. Upon hearing that I was from 'Jhelum', he joked and assumed it meant 'Mirpur'. It happens all the time. Jhelum is situated between the capital Rawalpindi and another key city, Lahore, and its borders lie very near to Kashmir. Mirpur is situated in Kashmir. For those who have no clue about this famous place, Mirpur is predominantly a rural area made up of small villages well known for their traditional thought. Amongst the educated *Urdu-speaking folk*, Punjabi speakers are deemed 'uncivilised and barbaric', and those from Mirpur are rated even more so. In fact the language of Mirpur is *Pahari*, a socially undesired spoken variety of Punjabi. A word-for-word translation would mean 'language of the mountains' where *pahar* means mountain. Therefore the idea is that those who live in the mountains are cut off from the rest of civilisation. This man's racist attitude was so unbelievable and unbearable to listen to. I felt I had to justify and defend myself even though I did not originate from Mirpur.

'Shall I call you next week?' he asked.

'Don't bother,' I replied.

Another highly intelligent man spent about twenty minutes trying to establish how many siblings I had and what they all did. Surely he wanted to know about me and not them? No. He was interested more to know whether we were a modern nuclear family or whether we had the traditional Pakistani average of six.

He then harped on about whether we spoke Urdu or Punjabi at home, and which I was better at.

'Why don't you just ask me if I am from Mirpur?' I asked him bluntly, tired of his skirting around.

'Well I was trying to be subtle.'

Clearly he needed more practice. He was an intelligent man; interesting, well spoken, articulate and all those things that I find attractive. Sadly though, his attitude put me off, in the way that the following guy did.

We had exchanged a few emails and spoken once. The next time he rang, I happened to be in the car park waiting for a lady to reverse out of a space so that I could park my car (just in case any police officers are reading this; yes I did have the hands-free kit!).

'What are you doing, haven't you parked yet?'

'I am waiting for a person to leave,' I replied.

'Kutta hai ya kutti?' [Is it a dog or a bitch?] he asked (i.e. is the driver male or female).

'Don't you worry about who it is but make sure you don't call me again. I don't have time for rude people,' I told him.

He sent a text message back with something very *polite* which I care not to remember. Manners feature very high on my list and he didn't have any.

And how can I forget the ones that refer to women as *toilet paper*. The guy at my college who confessed this to me went on to read for a degree. I believe he is now married to a girl from abroad because girls from the UK, in his opinion, were 'corrupt'. He himself had had relationships, but obviously it was unacceptable for women to do the same.

How terribly sad that we take it upon ourselves to judge women without knowing them, or anything about them or their circumstances? A friend of mine, Ghazala, when I first got to know her, had been looking for four years.

'*Four years*! I hope I am not left waiting that long,' I used to say to her.

'You won't be, or at least you shouldn't be,' she replied. 'I am divorced and when men hear that, they hear the word *diseased*. They think I have leprosy or something.'

After Ghazala's wedding night, the very next day, her husband told her that he didn't love her and that he hadn't wanted to be with her in the first place. The pain and heartache that she must've endured, no one can ever imagine. They were both graduates, born and bred in this country, so it wasn't a case of an arranged marriage of two people from conflicting mindsets.

The marriage dragged on for six months as she desperately tried to make it work but in the end they went their separate ways, leaving her firmly stamped with the stigma and label of being a *divorced* woman. It is difficult enough being a single Pakistani woman, never married and trying to find a partner; the experience for a divorced one must be horrific. She related one instance where the guy was obviously a jerk. When she refused to kiss him the first time she met him, he told her that he wasn't surprised that she was divorced. Another time she recalled a guy who halfway through the conversation realised that she was divorced. He had assumed that she was single even though it said clearly on her profile that she had been married previously.

'I am sorry. I don't want a *divorcee*,' he told her.

He was divorced himself.

And these are professional men …? More like professional losers.

What does Islam say about divorced women? Marry them, be kind to them, cast them not off as rejects. Muhammad (*salallahu alayhi wa sallum*) encouraged the marrying of divorced women whilst condemning the societal stigma of these women. Sadly, culture does the opposite.

Playboys

I met the Pakistani Hugh Heffners too. A friend of mine was having great difficulty meeting a decent enough guy (… which just about sums up the predicament for all women seeking partners). She would cry on my shoulder and I could sympathise; I was in the same situation. However, I don't like to see people cry and the downfall of being a matchmaker by nature is that as soon as I hear someone is single, my brain goes into overdrive and starts to scan the hardware folders for someone suitable for that person. It's just something I do without even thinking, so I asked another friend, Zehba, if she knew anyone for my friend.

By that stage we (I mean a handful of us) had decided that the Internet route did not work. However, we could still harness the benefits of cyberspace and build a network of friends who were either looking for themselves, or knew someone who was looking. In fact, that is how Zehba and I got to know each other. It was fate actually. I had just joined one matrimonial site and began to receive new profile alerts; the idea being that the database matched you with suitable profiles of the opposite sex.

On one occasion, after receiving a particular profile, I ran to the bathroom to check if I was still female. There had been a problem with the system and by accident they had sent me another female's profile. I read her details and thought of a male friend who seemed to fit the criteria she had specified. I contacted her explaining the situation and suggesting my friend. From there we struck up a friendship and she is now a very good friend of mine.

As it happened, Zehba rang me one day and put forward a friend of hers whom she hadn't seen for years.

'I bumped into him the other day, and he was saying that he is ready to settle down.'

I took his number and told her that I would be calling him first. If I felt that he wasn't an idiot and really was serious about settling down then I would give him her number. If I felt that he wasn't looking for marriage then I didn't want my friend to go through any more unnecessary heartache. We agreed, and I contacted him.

He seemed pleasant enough, passed my strict psychometric testing and so I forwarded my friend's number to him. He rang me a few days later explaining that they spoke on the phone but he felt that there wasn't a 'rapport' with her and that he wouldn't be pursuing.

'… I like you though …' he said.

By that time my search was on hold while I got my act together. Besides he wouldn't be interested in me; I would be too spiritual for him. He also made it clear that he wanted a drop-dead gorgeous woman where personality, education, interests were not important and that put me off him instantly. He admitted to wanting a trophy and that was it.

'Women are like cars,' he said. 'I want to know that I have got the top of the range.'

To this day, I cannot believe he said that but, sadly, men do see women as cars. My brother had an old LP from the 80's where the artist made a similar comparison in one of his songs.

Initially, when Zehba told me about him, she had mentioned his wild lifestyle, but insisted that he had changed and that now he was more spiritual. Of course this meant that he now said *'Salaam'*.[11]

We spoke and I explained that I would not be the sort of woman that he would be interested in.

'What do you want from a man?' he asked.

'I want a fairytale,' I confessed. 'I want my prince to come on a horse and say to me, *I have waited for you all my life. You're mine, and I have come to get you.*'

'Meet me and if I like the look of you I will say that,' he replied.

Unimpressed by his response, I resisted but despite my resistance, he wouldn't go away.

'Give the man a chance will you, and stop making judgements on him,' Varsha told me, seemingly having fallen for his charms too. 'I think he scares you, because he might be normal and doesn't have the usual baggage that you always fall for.'

Maybe she was right; I had been wrong with everything so far so I took her advice and met him. Afraid to hear that I

---

11 The Islamic greeting meaning *'Peace to you.'* This is also one of Allah's Beautiful Attributes: He is *As-Salaam*, The Forebearer of Peace, so *'Salaam'* denotes spreading His Peace.

wasn't the model he was looking for, I introduced him to the sister of another friend who took a real fancy to him. He was conventionally good looking and, coupled with his Casanova charm, he was quite a stud.

Nothing came out of his liaison with her though, which I cannot understand as she was attractive herself. This just convinced me more that he was after a drop-dead gorgeous woman.

'It's not that,' he told me. 'I am after the whole package. She was ok looking, but she didn't have a magnetic personality. A brain is important too.'

I introduced him to a few more girls (with brains coming as standard) but he was too fussy. One of the girls even gave negative feedback that he was a pervert and she wasn't interested.

On one occasion, he rang and the conversation became slightly inappropriate so I got off the phone. We spoke a few days later and I apologised for sounding 'frigid' but asked that he refrain. He did. But soon after, the same thing happened. I decided that it was time for me to help him help himself. So, I put a profile for him on a matrimonial site and left him to channel his libido towards other women who would welcome it.

Six months later, he contacted me again. It was a total surprise as I had almost forgotten about him. I told him that I didn't want to play games and there was nothing that he had to say that I wanted to hear. He wasn't a friend, and I didn't need one. Either he married me or left me alone.

'Let's see what happens,' he replied, raising my hopes for nothing.

Within the coming weeks, I really did think that he was interested in me, but as always, I was the fool. I saw him a few times, but I think he couldn't make his mind up. I did the honourable thing and tried to find him someone. I took his profile to a different site and left him to his own devices. He said he wasn't interested in those girls but I thought to test him. When I created his profile and created a new email address for him, I told him to change his password, which he didn't. He knew I had access to the accounts and it didn't bother him.

One day I logged into the email account and I found pictures of naked breasts just staring at me. A girl from the site had sent them to him, I presume upon his request. It gave 'send me a *pic*' an entirely different meaning altogether.

I deleted the guy from my life. He would never change and I wasn't going to wait around to find out if he would. Weeks later he rang me at 4 a.m. The phone just kept ringing. I did not answer it. In the morning I saw five missed calls on it. He never rang again.

I am glad.

Slick Pythons

I have had the pleasure of this variety too. There was one in particular who was indeed a slick python. In those days I was actually flattered when men told me that my profile sounded interesting. Now I realise that this is probably just a universal icebreaker or something that is said out of politeness.

We had spoken on the phone and it seemed that we were made for each other. I had not been looking that long, and it was easy to end up talking for hours and hours on end. He had decided that I was '*the one*' after the first half-hour that he had spoken with me.

We had arranged to meet the next day, and he didn't want to get off the phone but talk to me *forever.* He was the same age as me, and that put me off slightly. From his conversation he obviously had a lot of growing up to do before he was ready to even contemplate marriage, especially to someone like me; I certainly didn't want to talk forever.

As the phone conversation progressed into the third hour (Don't you just hate that? I know friends who say, 'W*e chatted all night long*.' I mean who in their right mind does that? When I talk to people, they can't wait to get rid of me after ten minutes), it suddenly dawned on him that he didn't know what I looked like.

'Yeah, but you will see me tomorrow.'

'What if I don't like you, physically?' he said, rather worried.

'Then I will go and throw myself under a moving train.'

'No, I am being serious. What if I don't find you attractive?'

'If you don't find me attractive, then you don't find me attractive; what is so bad about that?' I asked. 'We are not meant to find every person attractive. Sadly, there will always be people that we don't find attractive but that doesn't mean that as people there is anything wrong with them. Besides, for every one person we don't find attractive there will be a handful of people out there who will find that person attractive,' I consoled myself.

'I really like the sorts of things you say,' he said like a child.

'So do I.'

'But I am really scared that I won't find you attractive, because I really like you as a person.'

'Well that is a judgement of Solomon that only you can make.' I felt like I was giving the guy much-needed therapy and that I needed to invoice him.

He said he felt comfortable with me. Proceeding to tell me how looks were very important to him, he narrated an experience with a girl whose photograph he had not seen but who 'sounded' attractive. (Exactly how a person can *sound* attractive, I will never know.)

They had arranged to meet and he had told her that he would be wearing a shell suit or something equally hideous along those lines. When I heard this, I asked if that was the case and if yes, then I needed to be terminating the conversation immediately; shell suits have got to be on MI5's Most Wanted List!

'I don't wear them. I wouldn't be caught dead wearing one. But the reason I said it, was that she would be looking for a guy who was wearing a shell suit. However, since her description of what she was intending to wear would be more or less true, if I liked the look of her, I would approach her and tell her that my shell suit was in the wash. If I didn't like the look of her, I wouldn't approach her.'

His logic was that he could stand next to her without her realising it was him because she would be searching for the guy in the shell suit.

'So what happened then?' I asked, grateful to be getting an invaluable insight to his character and real personality.

'Well, she turned up and she was damn ugly so I just went to the café opposite and watched her. She waited for a whole hour, just standing there, waiting for a guy with a shell suit, when all that time I was right there in my Gucci. It was hilarious!' Then he burst out laughing.

'Don't you think that was rather cruel?'

'I felt bad but I didn't find her attractive,' he said sheepishly.

'Do you have sisters?'

'Yes, I already told you.'

'Well you know what? I hope that no one does that to them.'

'They won't. My sisters are attractive,' he laughed.

'Well that is good; pity your personality isn't.'

I refused to meet him the next day, and if that girl is reading this, then my sister, there will be a man out there who will extend the respect to you that you deserve. If you haven't found him yet, you will one day. If you have … well there you go!

A few months later, a friend of mine met someone.

'He took me to this restaurant and confessed that he brought all the women that he met to the same place. The waiting staff had come to know him well and were laughing and he knew this, and he was laughing too whilst telling me that they called him a gigolo. Then he spent almost the whole afternoon eyeing up the waitress and said, *I feel bad that I am making comments at her, while I have invited you here.'*

She had met the same guy. To make things worse, I found out months later that a friend of a friend was seeing someone and that he had told her that he wanted to date exclusively with a view to marriage because he was serious about her. She then found out that this was a line he was also using elsewhere too. It was also the same guy.

Fortunately, everything in life has an opposite. So now let's turn our attention to all things nice.

Fifteen: Nice – Biscuits, Girls & Guys

The other day, as I walked away after my meeting, it occurred to me that I may have left my mobile on the desk. I went back to get it and I heard a member of staff, whom I knew and who had seen me talking to her colleague, come up and say to her, '*Oh, she is such a nice person.*'

As they stood there talking about me, I walked away frustrated at the idea of being 'nice'.

How I hate that word. I am sick of being 'nice'. For as long as I can remember, I have been the *nice* girl. Sometimes girls next door want to move away from home too! I want to be that woman that mothers warn their sons about; I want to be the opposite of nice. I don't want to be nice. It's not nice being nice!

In the way that *nice guys always finish last*, nice girls do too. Our mothers may think that men want to marry nice girls, and guys' mothers may tell them that they should marry nice girls, but I sometimes wonder about that. Do men *really* want nice girls? Don't men want it all? – The graceful lady in public, the insatiable sexual animal in the bedroom, the gourmet chef in the kitchen and the Prada-wearing devil in the boardroom.

When I first started looking, I had a dislike for the *nice* guy. Many times, a friend tried to introduce me to 'nice guys'.

'Just forget it,' I would tell her.

I had this image that they would be boring and unexciting. Forgive me for my ignorance, but this point is highlighted well by the champion of all single women, Bridget Jones herself. No singleton book is complete without a mention to Miss Jones so I will not deviate. With particular reference to the last scene in the movie, where Bridget (played by the actress Renée Zellweger) is kissing the handsome Mark Darcy (Colin Firth), she stops for a moment, looks at him and asks him whether nice boys kiss the way he is kissing her. She of course is left surprised by his incredible kissing ability!

Sadly, for most of us 'nice' = boring. (I have just realised that since I have been nice all my life, I am boring … That must explain why I am single. Oh how depressing.)

I even said to someone once, *'Look, you are a nice guy.'*

'Do you want a bad boy?' he asked me. 'Women say that to me all the time,' he went on. 'But this is where your theory falls down. You all think that you want a bad boy when in actual fact all you want is a nice guy to behave daring.'

Maybe he was right. What is 'nice' anyway? Perhaps the key is to first define the word? This puzzles me about language. Why is it that when you talk to people about this, as I have done many times, they always say 'define nice'. I mean if I can pick up the dictionary on my desk (which happens to be the Chambers 9th Edition) and tell you that 'nice' means:

'Agreeable; delightful, respectable, good in any way, satisfactory (often used as a vague commendation); (of a person) good natured, friendly, kind; delicate, dainty, foolishly simple.'

…Then why don't we all follow that definition? If a dictionary is supposed to be a catalogue of words and their meanings then why do dictionaries the world over differ in the meanings that they carry of the same words? And why do people turn around and tell me that we have our own ideas as to what constitutes *nice*?

My niece, when she was four years old, once asked, 'What does ugly mean?'

'It's something that is not nice,' I told her.

She was horrified.

'You're not ugly! You're nice!' she said.

One man even asked me to marry him, on the basis that I was a 'nice' girl. Months after I started walking on a more spiritual path, I received an email from the lady at the talk I mentioned earlier in this book. A semi-paralysed Muslim woman, a wheelchair user, had asked if there was anyone willing to stay the night and help her seek *Layla-tul-Qadr* [A Blessed Night found during the last ten days of *Ramadhan*, the Muslim month of fasting].[12]

---

12 *Layla-tul-Qadr* is the Night of Power when God's Mercy is at its peak. The extract below describes with great eloquence this auspicious night:

'There is perhaps a higher purpose behind Allah's choosing the night (*Layla-tul-Qadr*) for the commencement of the final revelation. The night is indeed conducive to quietness, serenity, peacefulness and tranquility; suitable for the nourishment of the soul.

… *Layla-tul-Qadr*, the Night of Power, the Night of Majesty, the Night of Grandeur, the Night of Dignity of Destiny and Determination. A night '*greater in value than a thousand months*'. A night celebrated by Muslims

I received that mail and knew that this was a test from Allah: Would I be willing to go help a stranger in need? Much to the objection of my mother, who was scared that this could be another joke someone was playing on me, I volunteered.

Luckily, it was not a joke and, since then, I go to see Bobby often; helping her with jobs around the house, teaching her what I know about Islam and in general spending time with her.

The second time I spoke with this guy, Bobby was in hospital and I was due to go see her the next day. He wanted to meet but I couldn't at the time that he suggested. When he asked why, I explained.

'Marry me,' he said.

'I am sorry?'

'I am serious,' he replied. 'How many people would take time out to go and see someone who brings no mutual benefit to them? I am asking you to marry me.'

I turned him down. Firstly, I hadn't even met him and there was no way I would let history repeat itself. Secondly, the first time that we had spoken he had made it clear that he had a problem with the fact that I wore the scarf but, since he

---

throughout the world, a night of historic significance marking the commencement of the final divine communiqué, a revelation that affected the fate of nations and their destiny, changing the course of history.

Layla-tul-Qadr carries with it 'peace until the dawn' implying that the realization of the sanctity of this night could act as a shield against all forms of things unsavory, improper; allowing those who live by what was revealed on that night to experience tranquility and peace with peace of mind.' © Sadullah Khan [full reference can be found in the Endnotes (ix)].

was having trouble finding a woman who would be willing to accept his young son, he reluctantly agreed to communicate with me.

He spoke of his ex-wife who was a typical *Pakistani beauty with green eyes*, and that he wanted personality this time. He had assumed that since I wore the scarf I was unattractive. Maybe I am, but he hadn't even met me; how can you make an instant judgement that covered women are automatically unattractive? As flattered as I was by his proposal, I deserved more than to be with someone who would 'be settling' for me.

There are also those who find it difficult to believe that Pakistani women living in the UK can be 'nice girls' too. How can we forget the way that certain old-timers (and even the new-timers) cling to the misconception that 'nice girls' are *not* the British-born Pakistani women. For them, their idea of a nice girl is the *submissive, pure woman* from 'back home'. Do these men not realise that some *submissive, pure women* from 'back home' are exactly the opposite to what they think? The number of stories you hear about women having sex in the village fields or men sneaking into their homes at night, despite the rigorous chaining of these young women, is astonishing. So a note to all people who still refuse to acknowledge reality – it is a fact that people will always find a way to satisfy their sexual desires irrespective of which country or society they originate from or happen to be resident in.

Thankfully, there are also those who do seem to believe, quite rightly, that it is possible to be a nice girl and have been raised in the UK. My brother passed on an email from a young lady who was looking for a wife for her brother. He had said that this reply came from nowhere a long time ago in response to an advertisement that had been placed at my father's request, but I think maybe there was a distortion of the truth here. As I had given up searching during that six-month period, I think the family thought that they would intervene, so this was more likely a recent move rather than some long-lost advert placed years ago. Anyway, the reply read:

'Me and my family are currently looking for a wife for my beloved brother.'

She went on to give a few details about her brother: how old he was; how tall he was; what he did for a living; a little about their family; where they were from – both the UK and Pakistan – and the fact that he had a fun-loving personality as well as a good sense of humour. He liked to keep himself fit and go to the gym regularly, enjoyed reading books and playing rugby. And that he sought someone committed to faith.

He sounded like a 'nice guy' but then so did each profile out there. But that was not the main issue. The thing was that in the way that I didn't want my parents looking for me, I was equally unreceptive to parents or sisters who were looking for a partner for their sons/brothers. They needed a nice girl who was welcoming to that approach. I was not one of them, though sadly, and to my horror, I was still a *nice girl*.

Nice guys, I am sure, go through the same trials and tribulations that nice girls do. A friend was in contact with a 'nice guy'. Attractive, trendy, intelligent, sociable and just like her, loved nights out,

'So what is the problem?' I asked.

'Well ... he drinks.'

So ...? It's not as if she was heavily into faith, and even if she was, so what?! Does drink make someone a bad person? For those who feel compelled to contact me and protest, maybe even tell me that I am not a 'proper' Muslim, my question to you is this – Who is the judge of man? God or fellow man? I feel that people jump too quickly on the *drink* wagon and fail to see the irony of other actions.

'We need to get our priorities straight,' Tariq once said. 'We won't think twice about booking a hotel room with that someone special yet we meticulously look at the packs of Polo mints to check the E-numbers.' And how right was he?

Drink is forbidden to Muslims, yes. However, there are many things that are also forbidden. But to judge someone merely on the fact that they drink, in my opinion, is a wrong thing to do. They may drink but maybe there may be mercy in that person's heart that is liked by Allah? This is a matter between that person and the Creator. Fortunately, as I mentioned earlier, the Divine is more forgiving than man ... but that should not surprise ... is He not *Ar-Rahman* [the Most Merciful], *Ar-Raheem* [the Especially Merciful]?

I once spoke with a guy regarding this, and he was astonished to hear what I had to say.

'Out of the dozens of women that I have spoken to,' he said, 'You are the first to say this, and I don't think that I will hear anyone say this ever again.'

He went on to say how he totally agreed and gave me the example of his father who had drunk alcohol all his life, and still did.

'My father was always condemned by most,' he said. 'He was not an alcoholic, but somehow, people couldn't accept him. And he (father) used to say, *'Arrey mein sharaab peeta hoon, kissey ka kattal toh nahi keeya!'* [I only drink alcohol, I haven't murdered anyone!]

Now this guy was proud to have a loving father which this man was. Did the fact that he drank alcohol make him less of a human being? Less of a father? And who had the right to judge and condemn him anyway?

In my own personal and very humble opinion, we should work on our own faith and character rather than rushing to decry others. Besides, the Creator adorns man with free will, so why should man try to take away that free will that has been bestowed upon him by the Divine?

Many times, I have been asked if I am looking for a 'practising man'. My response is that his relationship with his Creator has nothing to do with me. Everyone has their own interpretation and choice of how they wish to relate to Him. I am aware of the 'marry for the sake of Allah', and there was a time when I thought any person who said His Blessed, Superior Name was someone who feared Him. Then life taught me that faith is something that you can never measure for it lies deep within the heart. And only the One Who

Created the heart has knowledge of the sincerity and fear and devotion that lies therein.

Said Muhammad (*sallalahu alayhi wa sallum*):

'Many a one fast but gain nothing from their fasting except hunger and thirst; and many a one pray all night, but gain nothing from their night prayer except sleeplessness.' (x)

Sadly, judging people is a major crime of which we as human beings are guilty. I know this all too well, perhaps more so since I started to wear the scarf. I have had an array of responses; most of them don't want anything to do with me, most are frightened of me, most feel that I won't fit into their lives; some even tell me that I am not their 'type'. I ask myself, *How can people make this judgement without knowing me? Without knowing what I think, how I think?*

It seems that I intimidate some by serving to highlight their own connection (or lack of) with the Creator. One young man initially seemed to be besotted with me. As soon as I threw in the spanner, he sent me a two-page email explaining how he didn't think that he was worthy of me, and how much he respected me and that how one day he would try and get to the level that I was at. I was left puzzled by this. All I had said was that I wear the scarf and thus observe *hijab*, I was not laying down expectations of him. But the fact is that the word '*hijab*' is loaded and carries a host of meanings for different people. He probably had in his mind all sorts of notions that I expected him to be a practising man or that I would force him to pray and that I probably spent all my time on a prayer mat myself, but who am I to force something on someone when I don't like anything forced on me?

Then there are those men who specifically look for *hijab* girls because they think that these girls are the perfect submissive wife material. The number of men who have told me that they wanted *someone like me* to help them improve; and that they don't want a 'Western' girl is interesting. I am often left thinking about this; I see myself as 'Western'. So ... does that mean that I have no right to see myself as having a connection with the One who created me? (Deep explorations here, I know.)

While we are on the subject of *the deep*, allow me to give you access to the deepest darkest corner of some women's world. The 'nice guy' is commonly thought of as the one who wears shirt and straight trousers as his casual wear. You know the ones who grow up to dress like your Uncle? Yes, them.

Well I had a cousin, a *nice guy* who wanted to marry me. And before people start getting all flustered at the thought of consanguineous marriages, yes this is a practice that is common amongst Pakistani folk. I would like to remind people that Albert Einstein married his first cousin, as did *Mr Evolution*, Charles Darwin himself; both had exceptional children.

Leviticus 18 of the King James' version of the Bible lists all forbidden sexual relationships; cousin relationships are not included. Similarly in the Qur'an, the guidelines are clear. Islam's Abrahamic cousin, Judaism, also does not interdict this. So religiously, this is not something that is forbidden. What has made it unacceptable is society itself. Shifts in societal attitude ensure what is acceptable and what is not.

As the www.cousincouples.com website states, most people are probably descendants of cousin marriages as civil laws banning this practice have not always existed. In modern-day American society, the cousin marriage taboo is inescapable yet, interestingly, former President Franklin Roosevelt was married to his cousin. Therefore before legislation outlawing cousin marriage came into effect in the United States, this practice was considered perfectly acceptable. Similarly, here in Britain, certainly up to Jane Austen's time, the consanguine marriage was an accepted norm. Jane's own brother married their cousin, as did Fanny Price, one of her characters in her novel *Mansfield Park*.

Back to my cousin who wanted to marry me. Now I wouldn't have a problem marrying a cousin for the fear of risk to offspring, but it was the familial politics that frightened me to death and so I turned him down. He was, and still is, a 'nice guy', now married, with lovely children. (Incidentally, he didn't marry any of our cousins in the end.) I saw him at a wedding recently and I thought in twenty years' time he will still be dressed like he is now; like his dad, my Uncle.

Let me give you another example. Many years ago, I arranged to meet a potential husband for that awful *coffee* routine. My timekeeping is atrocious but whenever someone is late, miraculously, I seem to arrive early. Perhaps it is a Law of Nature; a little bit like when you are stuck on the motorway and the lane next to you is moving steadily ... so you cleverly decide to change lanes only to find that you should've stayed in the one you just came out of, because it is now moving and the one that was moving is now stationary!

We were supposed to meet for 4 pm. He text messaged saying he would be late and so, naturally, I got there for 3.42 p.m. Not a big deal, I could make up for my surprise punctuality by roaming the streets for the odd twenty minutes. So I went window-shopping (… of course!).

4.35 p.m. – Came the message that he would be another half an hour late. Although slightly frustrated, I appreciated that sometimes these things are out of our control. I like to think that when I am late then someone would have the compassion to wait for me.

5.12 p.m. – He texted again, apologising. Something had happened and he was looking at a further delay of forty-five minutes or so. If I did not want to hang around, he would not expect nor ask me to; that he would 'understand'.

Obviously, there was a serious problem here. I had come all this way to see him, and it would be foolish to make an hour's journey home, when I could get this out of the way by hanging around a little longer.

'I don't want to inconvenience you,' he texted back.

'Don't worry about that, I have waited long enough. Just hurry up please,' was my reply.

5.45 p.m. – He called to say that it was best that we didn't meet, as he was unable to get away. I asked what the reason was and he said that his sister-in-law needed to go shopping and he had to take her. That is where he was; waiting for her.

I was furious! Scenarios of little old lady/explosion/ children/hurricane were running about in my mind, when all that time, he had kept me waiting just because someone couldn't be bothered to take a taxi or the bus!?

A part of me wanted me to say, 'Forget it!' Any other normal person would have. Someone I know had just got off the train, found out that the guy she was supposed to be meeting was running ten minutes late, and so she hopped on the same train, which was going back and came home! As much as I wanted to dive into the phone, reach the other side and strangle him there was no way I was going to let him off. I had just spent one hour and forty-five minutes or so going into the same shops over and over; even had security at House of Fraser send out an alert about someone suspicious matching my description, and I was not about to budge until I saw this spineless wonder.

It was obvious from where I was standing that he didn't want to see me, and to be honest I had no burning desire to see him either as his actions had successfully led him to the reject bin, but I wanted him to turn up so that I could give him a piece of mind (free of charge).

'Are you sure?' he said, slightly worried as I told him that I was not going anywhere.

Oh I sure was all right! I even was prepared to go buy a sleeping bag and wait all night if I had to. He tried to worm his way out of it by suggesting that out of respect to me, he didn't want to inconvenience me any longer as he didn't know how long he would be. I told him to put respect to the side for a moment, as after that afternoon, it had been truly exhausted. So, he said that by 6.30 p.m. he would *try* and get there.

6.15 p.m. – Miraculously, he called and said that he was at the tube station. I had planned to meet him, say hello, tell him that he was a waste of space and just walk off, so I made my way over there ... To find Mr *Nice* Guy with straight trousers, awful shirt and hideous tie. He looked so harmless that I didn't have the heart to shout at him or walk off. So we went for 'coffee'.

We sat down, he got the coffee (and paid for it!), and then we talked. He was extremely shy and just kept apologising. Despite my anger and frustration, I was pleasant to him and after a while he was more relaxed. Unfortunately, by that time I had finished my coffee.

'Thank you very much. Good to see you and bye,' I then got up.

'But ... you just got here.'

'Well ... it's now 7p.m. We were supposed to meet at 4 p.m. If you had made an effort to not mess me around, I could've spent more time gulping coffee that I don't even like,' I told him. 'Next time; either tell her a time that is five hours in advance of the time you are intending to turn up or just admit that you don't want to meet her rather than play games; which you seem to be terrible at anyway. This is not how established professionals should behave,' I added.

He apologised and acknowledged that this was his 'first time', and didn't know how to approach it. As flattered as I was that I was his *first*, I didn't want the responsibility of breaking him into the matrimonial search etiquette. I know that Pakistanis (or even South Asians in general) are notorious for our inexcusable timekeeping and we have our own classification of what constitutes 'ten minutes', but this guy really did enrich the meaning of '*Sorry I am late.*'

I came home, disappointed. Disappointed that my experiences were dead ends every time and if this is what was left for me then how sad it all was. The girls and I sat down for the autopsy.

'Nasreen, this does not surprise me one bit. For your own sake start being selfish,' Varsha told me with great concern.

Zehba also said that I was too soft. That and I had 'no standards'. She herself had strict criteria – must be 5'10"+; must have full set of hair; must be from the *Raja* caste; must have at least two cars; must have own home; must not have been married before; must not have kids and so the list was endless.

So during my six-month break from the matrimonial scene, I reflected upon all my experiences so far and decided that I needed to stop being Miss Nice. I was ready to go back to searching for husband/friend/lover/father of children (preferably all the same man). But this time, I wouldn't be heading for a pond or a canal or a river bank, like I had been thus far.

This time I would head for uncharted waters.

Sixteen: Bait

The quality of the matrimonial websites I had been using was fairly poor. So I was extremely glad when I stumbled across a new website. This seemed to be of higher calibre, which was good news for me. All I needed now was a new profile.

'Describe your personality, hobbies, ambitions and goals,' the guidelines stated. I was doomed already; talking about me was one of the most difficult things on the planet. What was I meant to write? What did other people write? I had a look at the female profiles as well as the male ones and they all sounded as if they were written by the same person.

I took my old profile and revised it taking into account my encounters so far. I needed to sift those candidates whose time I would only be wasting and therefore I began to write:

I don't believe in stringing a whole load of adjectives together to describe myself, because that makes the ads sound near enough the same (!), and in essence, others may not agree with what I may think; only the One who created me knows me best.

What I can say is that like any person, I have my strengths and weaknesses, confidence and fears, dreams and hopes. I have touched many heights of success and many depths of disappointment too. By the Grace of Allah, may He be Glorified, I have had everything [and much more] than I could have imagined, dreamed, wanted or hoped for and yet there is that one piece of my life which is missing; I am an ordinary girl looking for an extraordinary guy . .

I am looking for a man who has that balance in his life, knows his priorities and knows when to work, rest and play. A man with strong arms, an intelligent brain, a warm heart and lots of courage (to put up with my slightly deranged sense of humour!); a man who will walk into my life and make all that is not so good, good and all that is good, better; a man who will let me do the same for him.

Anyone into RnB, hip hop, garage and other bad boy/rude boy stuff, please refrain from replying.

Fans of Bollywood, Pollywood, Lollywood need to seriously think about their taste.

Those in pursuit of worldly possessions and high society kindly do not contact me.

Anyone in his 40s/50s, please think about it and then not reply.

Any 'players' should also save their time.

Those hung up on caste please invest your time else-where.

Anyone stuck in traditions & 'culture', please stay there, since there is no room for any in my life.

Anyone who uses the word "Islam" to hide behind his own insecurities; good luck to you.

[I do apologise if my words seem harsh, but I have to be honest].

Please do contact if you are looking for substance in your life, if you strive for peace of mind and heart, and have intentions to constantly develop as a human being. You do not have to be practising and, even though I am fairly Islamically inclined, I am still open minded so am not going to force anything on you!

Please do contact if you want a companion to help you attain the felicity of *Jannah* [Paradise] ... those looking for 'Happily Ever After' ... well this is it!

Please do contact if you are looking for someone who will endeavour to be everything a man could want in a woman.

Please do contact if you want someone to look after and are prepared to understand her when she sometimes doesn't understand herself!

Please do contact if you waited all your life for someone who has waited for you in the same way ...

Should you wish to reply to me then I would love to hear from you and, if not, then may you find the one for you – but please don't forget to say a little prayer for me too.

Thank you.

Seventeen: Inspired By

During our lifetime we come across people who in some way or another will touch our lives. By the same token, we also live the life of this temporary world by touching the hearts of strangers, without even realising.

I wanted to devote a separate chapter (because my acknowledgements section would've just overflowed) to all those men who through their kind words have left me in awe of the mercy that is found in the human heart. These men I never had the pleasure of meeting and I will never know who they were, but it was their passing comments which left imprints on my heart, and for that I shall be grateful for all of my days.

My profile that you have just read caused quite an unprecedented response which turned out to be just a fraction of the wonderful comments that I would go on to receive over the next phase of my search. One reader was so moved by my request for a little prayer that he sent me the following message which was both his first and his last:

'I pray for you the one who will be coolness for your eyes, the contentment to your heart and the strength to your *Eeman* [faith].

Ameen' [God please accept this supplication]

Only I will ever know how much those words touched the very depths of me; I couldn't have asked for a better prayer. Another gentleman's words also left me astounded:

'*Salaam*, Not sure I'm suitable for you (if only I was a better person and maybe a little younger) what you wrote was deeply touching. I just had to say: you have a beautiful mind and soul, Praise be the One to whom we shall all return. may Allah find you a compan—'

The message was incomplete because the site only allowed a certain quota of letters as initial contact. How could I not reply to this person! I replied to each and every single person who contacted me, even if I was not interested. I felt that everyone deserved some sort of acknowledgement. So I wrote to him:

Well ... What can i say? We don't realise the value of words. I thank you for yours. May Allah, Exalted is He, reward you for the little bit of joy that you brought into the life of a stranger.

You said that you weren't sure whether you were suitable for me, you made a comment about being younger, but what I couldn't understand was this thing about a better person. Your modesty is impressive.
What state my mind and my soul are – like it says in the profile, only the One who created me knows me best;

but I pray that when I find myself standing in front of Him, He is pleased with me and I look forward to that moment with every breath I take.

Like I always say; we are all lost souls hoping that somewhere along the line we find someone who rescues us, *in sha Allah* [God willing], we all find that companion one day, and if not on this earth, then surely they wait for us in the Life Yet to come. And His Promise is true.

I am currently speaking with someone at the moment, what will happen, only He knows, and I regret that I cannot speak to you at this moment in time. I endeavour to reply to every single person who replies to me; there is no need to be rude, even if you are not interested in them.

I am not saying that I would not be interested in you, surely, how can a woman not be interested in a man who has truly made her heart smile like you have.., and I wanted to write these few words for you, since the personalised messaging thing only lets you send messages of a certain length, and well, my essay would not fit into that!!!] but i hope you can understand that at this particular moment in time I feel inappropriate to be speaking to others, when Allah, may He be Glorified, has sent perhaps a remarkable man into my life.

However, if the future proves that this man is not for me nor I for him, and should you still be available, and if that is ok with you, perhaps I can get in contact with your good self? [I do wear the scarf.. however if that is an issue, then I will completely understand].

No one knows what the future holds, except the One who holds the future. Perhaps our paths will cross again, perhaps they will not, but whatever it does hold; I pray for you the best in all that you do.

I leave you in the care and protection of the One who created you, me and all that exists.

Nasreen
[An extraordinary guy's ordinary girl]

He replied:

'Thank you so much for taking the time to write to me…. I've been thinking for a few minutes about the most suitable and appropriate words that describe what I think and feel about what you wrote, but…..anyway please forgive me as I can only say what's in my heart: Sincere, sublime, intelligent, gentle……. reflecting an open, beautiful heart filled with *eiman*.
We have an expression in my language that loosely translates:

"that which arises from the heart lands or settles on the heart".

And when it is inspired by, and has the smell and colour of, *eiman* it touches the soul too.

You don't often expect to be inspired by a few words that someone writes about themselves (certainly not on an internet matrimonial site) but when you are, then it's natural to wonder if you'd be good enough for such a person, it's not false modesty, lack of confidence or indeed flattery.
If I was uncertain about my suitability, I am very certain that these marriage sites are beneath someone like you.......but then again........
I often remember something a great great man once said: "of all the characteristics of this world, only one appeals to me, that it is passing, fleeting".

SubhanAllah [All praises be for Allah] and *alhamdoliAllah* [All thanks and praises are for Allah] for your open, free heart and mind (prerequisites to true *eiman*), subhanAllah and alhamdoliAllah for your spirituality, subhanAllah and alhamdoliAllah for your modesty, subhanAllah and alhamdoliAllah that you wear hijab, subhanAllah and alhamdoliAllah that you do not wish to speak to more than one man at the same time.

I pray if the man to whom you are speaking is meant for you and deserving of you, that your path to marriage and happiness is painless and joyous. And if it turns out that he is not meant for you. it would truly fill my heart with joy to hear from you, even if it was to be only an exchange of words and thoughts.

May Allah guide us and put us on the path that earns his pleasure even if we don't always recognise that path.... and if we recognise it and do our best to stay on it then we are already rescued.......*inshaAllah*.
I pray that he may firstly keep your eiman safe, and that he always watches over you.

It has truly been a privilege.

F.
[An inspired soul]'

At that moment my heart was elsewhere but time would reveal the oceans to be too far apart for me. I then contacted this person again in the hope we could explore if we would be suitable as lifetime companions. He replied:

'I can't remember the last time I was this happy and a bit sad at the same time............ happy because I've heard from you, and a bit sad because things have probably not worked out for you.'

He then went on to reveal more about his life; his children and his aspirations. Here was a man who might be all that I was seeking, but there was something that was not letting me proceed with him. It was inexplicable at the time, but makes perfect sense now. The man because of whom I was hesitant (who for all I knew, had left my life), unbeknown to me, would return when I least expected him to. You can read about it in a chapter to follow, titled 'Oceans Apart'. But at that particular juncture of my life, I didn't have the knowledge that the future would eventually shower me with. So I wrote to Mr *Could Have Been Right:*

My sincere apologies for the delay in responding

Friday-Monday I had a friend from Birmingham who came to stay with me. So I have been rather occupied but I did pick your email soon after it was sent, and hand on heart, I guess I could have replied but I hesitated.

The truth is that I didnt know what to say, I suppose I wanted to get my thoughts together in my head. In your last email to me, you talked about how spiritually drained I seemed. *Subhan'Allah*! I guess that is true. I would add to that emotionally drained too.

I am an upfront kind of person, I don't believe in deceiving anyone simply bcos I don't like to be deceived. So I have to be honest, there is something inside that makes me feel that I shouldn't be communicating with you.. deep down I think that I have come to want someone else. That guy I was talking to - well he went abroad for a while and he told me not to wait for him, but the truth is that i have tried to carry on, but it isn't working.

I am the kind of woman, who for the right man would drop everything, put my trust in Allah, and go live up my duties to my husband. I am not hungry for material wealth, I dont need anything, nor am i stuck in society, so i am ready to have my vows, right now, as i am typing this email to you, in fact.

That is why I feel that I cant email you, bcos perhaps I cannot offer you the above since I am perhaps pining for someone else.

Until I sort my heart out, and ask Allah *azza wa jall* [Glorified and Sublime be He], to control it for me, and give me the strength patience and courage to get through this so that He may reward me with the ease and relief quickly, I suppose I am not ready to seriously talk with anyone.

So I don't know the right thing to say to you.

He replied:

'I am so sorry that you have a broken heart............
I promise you that it will heal in time. What advice can I
give you??.............. I guess you'll already know
everything I'm about to say, but sometimes it can be
refreshing to hear it from someone else.

Pray to Allah.....pray that (though already high) He
elevates the position of His greatest blessing to man
kind, namely Mohammad salalla alayhi wa sallum and
that he showers him with his salaam and blessings, and
immediately pray that he guide you and grant you
patience .... you will find that he is too great
and compassionate to answer one part of your prayer
and ignore the other.

I agree with you that you are not ready to talk "seriously"
with anybody, or to search matrimonials or write/reply
to messages.......you need a break..........as, I have no
doubt, you know a muslim lady's greatest possession and
ornament is her modesty. I hope you will take the above
advice, from a humble person in Islam, in the spirit in
which it's given.
Let me tell you a story:

I have spoken to 5 or 6 ladies, and most of them have
asked how I came
to choose this website? and I'll tell you what I've told
them:

Since my separation and divorce, I was uncertain about finding my life companion, but as time went by I felt sure that it was what I needed...........one day I typed "muslim marriage" in google and to my
surprise there were all these sites dedicated just to that.
so I started browsing..... looking at peoples profiles(male and female), what they'd written about themselves, their lives, aspirations......... all very
interesting.......one day I visited this website and came across this lady's
profile, and I was amazed by how beautiful I found it and how deeply it
touched me, it wasn't the particulars of what she'd written but the
spirit that shone through it, which gave a clue to her beautiful mind and
soul.........I found myself visiting this website everyday just to read what
she'd written........it inspired me so.until I just had to let her know what
I thought of her and wish that she find a worthy compa- nion. to my
frustration I could not do that, unless I registered and became a member.......so that's what I did and after I'd sent her the short message I felt calm and con- tent...............

I haven't said these things to you, so that you will go Ahhhhh, but

simply to show you a reflection of yourself, of the kind
of person you are/can be and of the beautiful potential
that you have within you.'

There were all sorts of emotion that flowed through me
when I read these words. I was a mere nobody yet my Creator
had honoured me immensely.

I hid my profile for a while because I was not ready to go out
there and continue with the matrimonial search. Then I
received the following mail:

'Well if you allow me to say few words about your
profile, even though your profile is not currently available, at the time when I was going through it I thought if
this person would choose to contact me first thing I
would do is to pass my comments/compliments about
writing of her profile.

It was very well worded, by the time I had finished
reading it I thought she is a very good writer and I will
ask her to try an write a book(not on profile writing)as I
see you have all the potentials to do so.

Factors of balance and clarity of speech, honesty and
rhythm were outstanding along with many others. I now
wish that I had printed it out and could makefew specific
references.

Even though your profile was one of the longest still it was one of very few of those, which I have read fully well, hope it will be back online soon.

I actually like people with blunt and brave approach that is what I found in there.

Well, I think I must stop it there, because I don't want you to say that I am good at buttering, but its not buttering and why would I do that?
That is exactly what I felt; it's rather the short version.

I think before I go I must make you promise one thing, and that is: if you really get inspired after reading my comments and finally decide to write a book, when its published hope you will not forget to fit my name some where in the book, may be under "Inspired by".

Please note that my name which you know of is not my real name, no I am unable to answer your question "What is my real name" at this stage, but if you do decide to sit down and write a book, promise I will give you my real name.'

*(I never did find out your real name but congratulations, you made it into the book under a chapter title that was *inspired by* you!)*

Even though I had hidden my profile, I was unaware that after a certain period of time, the profile would automatically become visible unless I set it to permanently invisible; which I had not done. I found the following message as the initial expression of interest in my profile while it was available for all to see and I was deluded into thinking that no one could see it!

'You are sounding true, First time I am seeing a true profile written on this site. It is true becos its has the harshness and softness, like life the two polarity. Take care. Allah Hafiz' [God is the Protector]

The young man was from abroad, and although I could've declined him, I needed to accept in order to send him a thank you for his message.

I am accepting you because I want to thank you for your lovely message. However you are too young for me. Secondly, even if you were older, I don't have the means to bring anyone over from outside the UK.

He replied back:

'Don't you think you had gone little far ,First in search of soul mate no need to market onself. This what comment people do on this world or site by seeing bank acc…age .country and social securities and that is the reason the suffer..

I saw the seed of love who is searching her soul mate, I may not be yr soul mate but I have tremendous respect for those who carry such kind of feeling within themselves and that was the only reason to write.

I would like to share my view on love which may help you in the future to search a soul mate for yourself. Love is the basic nourishment for the soul just body can't live without food and mind cant without oxygen and the soul cant without love. There are millions of people on the earth but very few have the soul. What I mean to is: their souls are still potential that have not become actual yet because they have not provided the right food for the soul to grow..

Learn the secret of loving so that you can have as much as love is needed for soul to grow.

Dear Nasreen do you know the difference between soul mate and so called conditional love which is based on bank acct ,age ,country etc. Soul mates enjoy the beauty of their presence. Sometime they sit silently, not doing anything but still communicating with each other in harmony of nature. Soulmates are eternal they will go to Jannah together...

On the contrary conditioned people even while sleeping together they don't enjoy of becoming one is thinking of

Julia Robert and other is about Tom Cruse. For them it just heeling and throwing the energy of sex.............they live still together for year... Its really funny........Many things to talk but..........

Allah will help you out in search of soul mate.. and my true wishes is with you...'

We exchanged a few more ideas but because I was beginning to be messaged by other people, I wanted to hide my profile. If I did that though it would automatically disable me from communicating with everyone including him. And I didn't want to be rude to him. However the search had now become slightly unbearable and so I logged on one day to delete my profile. There I found sentiments from him that I will take to my grave:

'Hi Nasreen u r trying hard in search of soulmate but in searching you wont get him you have to wait and see, he will not knock the door of your heart he will simply enter in your soul then you will realise.......'

Eighteen: Soulmates

Ask anyone what a 'soulmate' is and they will come up with at least a hundred viable definitions. Back then, I always thought that it meant the *'one you loved; your partner,'* but that was before I spoke with people and gauged their thinking. According to many, 'soulmate' can be anyone with whom you have some sort of connection.

The Collins Gem pocket dictionary (in my pocket of course) defines the 'soul' as:

'Spiritual or immortal part of human being'

When I look up the word 'mate' it tells me:

mate[1] comrade, husband, wife, one of pair, officer in merchant ship; *inf*. common Brit and Aust. term of address, esp. between males – v. marry; pair – **ma'tey** a. inf. friendly, sociable.
mate[2] n/vt *Chess* checkmate.

So for argument's sake, and as eminent Linguistics Professor Roy Harris tells me, words don't have fixed meanings. We as users of language attribute meaning to them depending on the context, our experience, our beliefs and so on. Thus as a user of this remarkable phenomenon called language, my definition of 'soulmate' is that person with whom you spend all of Eternity. Now for those who do not believe in the concept of Eternal Paradise, of course my definition will be render meaningless.

Read the thousands of singles' profiles and you are likely to find the word *soulmate* somewhere. It seems that we are all looking for a soulmate. Nobody wants just a companion, friend, spouse or partner for procreation. No.
Everyone wants a *soulmate*.

'The thing about soulmates is that I think we rarely get to meet them,' said one interesting man. 'But they are out there.'

Now he was quite an enchanting character and for a moment, I thought he was my *soulmate*.

This man had captured me instantly with his profile. There was something about him; something I couldn't put my finger on. You know how on those rare occasions you know that you have just experienced some kind of wonderful, something that you just cannot explain, but you know that you have experienced it and that it was something? Well, when I met him that is how it was surreal.

The morning after the night before I opened my eyes and, as I lay in my lonely bed, I saw reality – my room, my bed, my things, my emptiness – and I knew that I was back to the real world; my world. The night before had felt like a dream, as if I had danced amongst the stars for a moment or two.

'It is better not to want something because you save yourself much heartache when you discover that you can't have it,' that is what I had told him.

I had felt a certain inexplicable pull towards him from the very first email and the subsequent conversation reinforced that. The next morning I suspected that I may have dreamt that conversation; that maybe he didn't really exist. If he did, most likely it was just one of those passing things for him and he would have probably forgotten my name already. So I tried to empty my mind from any thoughts about him.

I was supposed to be meeting someone else that day too and he told me to contact him after the meeting was over. When it was, I hesitated. Not that I didn't want to call; it's just that I was afraid. He didn't exist, right? Surprisingly he did and when he called it convinced me that he did. At the same time reality came knocking and that old adage of *stunning woman* reared its head and I felt disheartened. But, despite that stumbling block, I set off to meet him.

I was enjoying the whirlwind element of it so much so that it didn't bother me that I was meeting him at his flat. I wasn't concerned about what might happen but I wondered whether he had a habit of inviting women to his place. What had happened was that it was late and all the places were shut. We could've met another day but I wanted to meet him as we had planned. Deep down I felt that he was decent, genuine. We had somehow 'connected' and even though it was indescribable, I went with that feeling.

I was so glad that we didn't do that whole coffee thing. It felt so right, as if I had known him for years. I liked how relaxed he was; the way he was dressed; he was just him at his most basic and I liked that. I think the dynamics of the matrimonial search do tend to be 'false'. People are too often on their best behaviour, wearing their best clothes, all *made up*. But I liked the way he didn't have a care in the world. It was comfortable.

As I sat there and listened to him, many things went through my mind. I could feel his honesty and openness. It came through even more when he told me that he missed the gentleness of a woman's touch. I secretly wanted him to feel my touch.

Then there was a point when I heard a silent click. For the first time in my life, I felt that my soul was at ease and had just connected with another. Maybe it was just a spark of a greater overall circuit because, to be honest, I had felt that right from the moment he opened the door, looked at me and smiled. There had been something in his smile. I was not attracted to him at all. Not even in the slightest, yet for some strange reason he was alluring. I felt as if knew him.

We talked about our experiences and I mentioned my natural photograph. He asked if I had the photo with me and as it happened I did. It was on my railcard. (Don't laugh please; I had spare copies so I put them to use!)

'I always wondered about you,' he said quietly. 'I always regretted not keeping in touch with you. I used to wonder, *what if?* and by then it was too late.'

What did he mean by that? … He took me back in time, asking if I recalled speaking with a certain man. He described his details and his profile and I was left speechless myself …

Whilst searching for a partner, you come across an array of people. Some you remember, some you don't. Some you choose not to. And then there are some that leave their mark in an inexplicable way. In all these years that I have been searching, I can truly say that only a few men that I have come across have left some kind of lasting impression on me. As it happened, this man and I had crossed paths once before ... a few years earlier.

I had enjoyed his correspondence back then and the feeling had been mutual. We had had quite a few email exchanges and every time I would receive his replies it was as if I had written them myself; we seemed to be so similar. He had sent me a photograph and although I hadn't found him *attractive*, I was still interested in him. I wanted to know him and was not too fussed about the way he looked. He had intrigued me and I wanted to know the man that he was, the one inside, and whether my soul could connect with his. After all, marriage should be the union of two souls, and with him, there was something there ... something I couldn't explain.

A photograph is never a real depiction of a person, as we all know. And only upon face-to-face interaction can you tell if you are attracted to a person. But alas we didn't get this far. My *au naturel* didn't yank his chain as I had expected but I thought that perhaps he would have the ability to see beyond that. He seemed an intelligent man and intelligent people know, or ought to, that anyone can look good in make-up. The whole point of the exercise was to sieve out the man who would be able to recognise real beauty. A man of intelligence and substance; he would be the one for me.

Alas the exterior was the essential prerequisite for him, as with most people, and I accepted that. I attributed him to be one of those run-of-the-mill professional guys with that proverbial *'good blend of East/West values'* – only I wasn't looking for that. I was looking for an extraordinary guy who would be happy with just an ordinary girl. I hoped it might be him but, sadly, it was not. He had talked about me possessing the personality but unfortunately lacking that very vital X-factor (i.e. drop-dead gorgeous looks) that foolish men seek. He believed, like many, that that was the key to a long-lasting relationship.

'Judge a book by its cover; yes,' I had told him. 'But also remember that there are many pages in between too.'

I advised him to at least have a five-minute conversation with someone before, quite rightly, moving on to the next vital hurdle of the *'pic'*. I am glad that with the passage of time some of the nonsense that I had said during that initial cyber encounter filtered through. When I sent him a message the second time around, he replied back and expressed an interest in speaking with me on the phone. My conversation impressed him so much that he wanted to meet me without the benefit of having seen a photograph. Thankfully, some good did come out of history. He was now able and willing to put to one side the pressing issue of looks and give personality a chance.

'Can I ask you something please?' I asked.

'Of course.'

'Was my photo really that repulsive?'

'Not at all,' he said. 'But that's men for you; we are shallow by nature.'

My encounter with this man was as bizarre as our previous one had been and we were left with more *what ifs*. We also knew that there were overt differences between us and that it could not work. As two people, as two minds, as two souls, we had the potential to be great together. But despite being similar and having that chemistry, as a couple facing the outside world, with completely different outlooks on life, we wouldn't have survived.

He talked about dating and a physical relationship at some point, but I didn't want a relationship based on lust or any intimacy at all, especially at that particular moment. It was dangerous.

'I am a woman, I am weak,' I told him.

'I am a man, I am weaker,' he said.

I left his place feeling stupid but it was something that I couldn't afford to get involved in. During our communication from way back then, for some strange reason, I would imagine a gorgeous wildcat with a diamond necklace around its neck, but in the way that I could never afford that animal, this man also came with too much of a high price.

It was late and he didn't even offer to walk me to my car. I was rather disappointed at that; a man who didn't care. Men are supposed to make us feel protected (… what is the point of having them around otherwise?). Maybe I did expect too much. He did walk me to my car in the end but only because I forced him. I thought it was the gentlemanly thing to do and that men of his calibre did so without seeing it as a burden or inconvenience.

Then I realised that the magic lay perhaps in the atmosphere and never really with either of us as I had mistakenly thought.

Nineteen: Send Me a 'Pic' (Part Two)

B y now, one thing was for certain – looks are everything. Parents demonstrate this notion perfectly when seeking marriage partners for their offspring. If they like the look of the guy/girl, they take it further; if not then they don't (quite logically). They hardly sit there exploring personality and character, do they? Well I found that most men employed the same technique.

One potential husband, after the usual pleasantries of *who what where how when*, suddenly started painting. Apparently in his mind, he had in front of him a canvas and he wanted to know which colours to use so that he could see a mental image of me. I helped him to paint a picture of the Hunchback of Notre Dame. He wasn't too impressed …

'Would you describe yourself as good looking?' has got to be one of the worst questions that anyone can expect you to answer. I mean, what are you supposed to say to that? What is *attractive* anyway? And *pretty* and *good looking*? If you say 'yes', then you must be arrogant. If you say 'no', then you must have low self-esteem. So can you ever win?

These days I go around describing myself as *'extremely good looking'* but back then, I didn't think that I could turn around and tell a man that I thought I was good looking, or pretty, or attractive because, at the end of the day, these were just words and, like any other, the bachelor ended up formulating his own conclusion irrespective of what I thought.

The more time went on, the more stubborn I became. I am sure that no one around me understood what the big deal was, but it mattered; it mattered to me. One of my greatest criticisms of the culture in which I was raised was that everyone was after the fair girls. Since skin tone is most often the distinguishing factor to attractiveness, it terrified me that there seemed to be no room in this culture for average sort of human beings. I told one potential husband that I thought looks attract initially but personality holds it there and he accused me of waving the '*ugly wand*'.

Was it asking too much to want someone who would love me, the real me and not just the packaging? I didn't think it was. I knew that if they met me, or saw me, they would be interested, but the real test was to see who could overcome that; for me that was real character.

Following the usual email and phone stage, I got talking to someone one night. We talked and talked and talked, which I guess is something that people do on the phone. We had really gelled somehow and the conversation seemed endless. The whole night had just flown past and we had talked so much that I thought my phone was going to burn, welding itself to my ear.

As the conversation drew to a close, he became a little nervous that we were going to meet the next day yet he had not seen a photo of me. This, he said, was something he would never dream of doing: meet without having exchanged photos.

I became nervous at that thought too. For I knew that all this time, all this bonding that had taken place would now be put into jeopardy. But I sent him my photo, neither asking for, nor seeing his.

I told him that if he didn't want to meet the next day then that was not a problem, he should let me know beforehand. Even a text message would suffice but preferably before I left my house as I didn't want to be left around waiting if he had no intention of turning up. I wouldn't waste anyone's time or be cruel and I expected the same. He said he still wanted to meet, albeit with a slight change in his tone.

The next day, we met up and I rang him to see where he was. I spotted him whilst still on the phone and had headed towards him. There I was, right there, in front of him, but he just looked straight past me – he thought I was a foreigner who was lost and needed directions. He was totally baffled and genuinely didn't realise that that was me. Then the penny dropped and he was quite shocked. Apparently, he thought that I was Spanish. It happens all the time. Sometimes people assume I am Italian. A few times I have been mistaken for being Portuguese; and since wearing the scarf, I am considered Turkish, even Iranian. Once someone thought I was Syrian.

'I can't believe it's you!' he exclaimed.

Being able to scrub up well is a blessing. He asked me why I sent a photo that really did me no justice. I asked him whether he would've met me had I sent the photograph and not spoken with him on the phone. He replied that he wouldn't have. I asked him if he would meet me if I had sent a photograph looking the way I looked, standing there in front of him at that particular point in time. He said yes he would.

'Ok,' I said. 'Just for the record, in both instances I am still the same person inside and those qualities that you have found in me have existed in me throughout even though outwardly I appeared different. The way I looked at that precise moment in time, I wouldn't look like that always, but yet the person, the woman I am, would carry on being me, who I have been all along.'

Verdict: Photographs can be misleading. I am sure many people will also agree that there seems to be an unofficial commandment in the world of the matrimonial search – *Thou shalt **only** put up photographs that are at least five years old.*

Maybe British Asian matrimonial websites would benefit by taking tips from the Western dating websites, incorporating into their Terms & Conditions that photographs must be recent. Why on earth do people bother putting up a photograph that is clearly the best one they have from when they were in their prime?

There was once a most handsome guy (or at least I thought), who had these amazing photos on his profile. We had exchanged emails and spoken on the phone. We hadn't met as I didn't want to be blinded by his good looks but instead wanted to pick his brains a little and see if there was any common ground. Days later, he said that he had put up another photograph, where he *'might look a little different'* … which he did.

In the first photos, he appeared to a model but in the later photo he was not. I blame my own stupidity; clearly, the ones that he had originally were taken in his youth. He must have been in his early twenties at the time. Then the most recent one he posted, which was more believable and realistic, made him appear closer to thirty-nine. (Yes I know; how could I get it wrong?)

We did speak a few times after that and soon it became evident that he had fabricated the truth a little too much regarding other things as well. Needless to say we didn't progress. I know that it is a generally accepted rule of thumb that most people online do not exactly fly the flag of sincerity, but it is still shocking nonetheless and a grave shame when that does happen.

Having been away from the online matrimonial scene for about a year or so, when I returned, I knew that I now needed a 'recent' photograph. I had had fun with the natural photo, and if nothing more, I gained valuable insight into a dangerous place called the male psyche. I let a friend take some photographs of me, but I refused to let her make me look like an overcooked chicken.

'Make-up to the bare minimum please,' I requested.

She agreed and so I agreed.

Little did I know that the politics of the *'send me a pic'* were indeed set in stone and that not much would have changed during my absence. Here is an interesting conversation:

Him – *Salaam*

Me – *wa-alaikum as-Salaam*

Me – how are you?

Me – could you excuse me a moment please

Him – sure

Me – i have to go get some water

Him – will wait

Me – i have just finished my bottle of evian

Me – i need to turn the alarms off and then run upstairs

Him – haha

Him – ok

Me – so if you hear

Me – the alarm going off

Him – do u have yahoo.msn?

Me – thru this msgnr thing

Me – then …

Him - :)

Me – YEP IT WAS ME

Me – waking up the whole world!!!!!!!!!!!!!!

Me – be back in a moment, *in sha Allah*!

Him – :-)

Him – *ameen*

Me – ok

Me – back again, out of breath, but back!

Him – wih water

Him – and no alarm

Me – and now you are gone!

Me – ha ha

Me – yes with water, a brand new 1.5litre

Me – am a water freak these days!!

Him – haha

Me – i tell you what

Him – do u have yahoo/msn?

Me – why dont we catch up another time

Him – :(

Me – i think you are talking to others ...?

Him – nope

Me – you can be honest, there is nothing wrong with that

Him – i went to take panadol

Me – but i find that

Him – if u have yahoo.msn

Him – will be better ;(

Me – [yeah,,, but i am hogging up the water!!]

Him – ;)

Him – u have a picture?

Me – yes

Him – can u send me

Him – :-)

Me – i have hidden it

Me – thought

Me – though

Him – can u send me?

Him – plz

Him – plz

Him – plz

Him – where is the pic :[)

Me – depends ...

Me – do i get the password to yours?

Him – on what?

Him – yep

Him – promise

Me – okay

Nasreen Akhtar

Him – send me yrs and I send u mine
Me – oh i see - we live in a cruel world
Him – :-)
Me – you scratch my back and i will scratch yours..
Him – yep :-)
Him – what is yr profession?
Me – i am a writer
Him – so u like poems ;)
Me – yes
Him – what stuff
Him – where is the picture
Him – am still waiting
Him – u r slow :-)
Me – i guess, i am fascinated by all writing
Me – you are too fast for me
Him – what do u write the most
Me – you are slowing me down
Him – where are the pictures
Him – still working
Him – :-)
Me – you are funny
Him – am I?
Me – but not as much as me..
Him – do u think am on TV show?
Me – ok, give me your email address
Him – am not gerry springer
Me – oh really - well i dont want to know you then
Him – where is the pic
Him – unhide it

Him – waiting

Him – singing

Me – will it be done instantly?

Him – waiting

Him – waiting

Me – la la la la

Him – waiting

Me – i am not listening

Me – la la la la

Him – waiting

Him – where is it

Him – where abt r u in London?

Him – quick

Him – waiting

Him – waiting!!!!

Me – do you always get what you want?

Him – :-)

Him – Not from writers usually

Him – tu parles le francais

Him – ?

Me – bien sur

Him – :-)

Me – habla usted espanol?

Him – spreakt ja nederlense

Me – neine

Me – or even nein

Him – deutche?

Me – haben zie platz frei?

Me – am sending you my foto,

Him – where is the pic

Me – so give me a few minutes,

Me – vous-etes pret?

Me – that is it you carry on talking to the others

Him – oui

Him – j'attends

Me – bien

Him – actually... am online coz of a work related issue... i am setting up a new business

Him – waiting for it

Him – :p)

Him – where is the pic

Him – pic

Him – pic

Him – pc

Him – plz

Him – plz

Him – plz

Me – that is a really original line

Him – do u wotk on TV?

Me – heard all of the exuses

Him – time stamp on email I got from my proposed business partner

Him – Patrik

Him – based in Naples

Me – give me your email

Him – u can contact him to chk ;)

Me – [i will be having words, with Naples..[!!!!!!!!]

Him – sure

Him – :-)
Me – and that Patrik person..
Him – waitig for pic
Him – still
Me – !!!!!!!!!!
Him – I used to be in Rico b4
Me – give me your email address
Him – moved to Sweden last yr
Me – je vous ai dit trente-six fois/
Him – where are the pic
Him – where are the pic
Him – where
Him – where
Him – want
Him – it
Him – now
Him – waiting
Him – w
Him – a
Him – i
Him – t
Him – i
Him – g
Me – where is my password..
Me – to aladdins cave??
Him – after u sent the pic
Me – ok … we will see
Me – ok…
Me – send me the password..

Me – [please!]

Me – ok., i have made visible the foto on the site

Him – am on the ph

Him – 1 sec

Me – ie you are talking to someone else

Him – patrik

Me – well now you know what i look like and i know what you look like

Him – u look cute :P

Me – *alhumdulillah*!

Him – u looked mine…

Me – what is cute?

Me – yes i have seen your foto

Me – it is a lovely foto

Him – and am ugly

Him – correct?

Me – no

Me – no one is ugly

Him – can i tell u something

Me – please do so

Him – u r very nice and want u as my friend

Me – i dont have male friends from this route

Me – but thank you for the compliment

Him – cant I be the first 1?

Me – no, sorry..

Him – online and phone pal for now

Him – ok

Him – nps

Me – no..sorry..

Him – sorry to have asked

Me – desolee

Me – pls dont be..

Me – hey, if you dont ask.. you dont get right?!!

Him – does that mean I shld stop chatting with u?

Me – but i will say in future, dont be so hasty to get to the foto stage

Me – some women want to feel that someone wants to know a little bit about them first

Me – that is why i hide my foto

Him – k… I guess u did not like my pic…

Me – people shouldnt be interested in you bcos of what you may/not look like

Him – I was joking a lot with… n considerd u as a friend

Me – I wanted to give you the benefit of the doubt,

Me – and I didn't want to be rude

Me – to you

Me– as I am not a rude person

Me – but your precipitant attitude for a foto is unappealing

Me – and especially the way you have gone about it

Him – appologize if i opened too fast

Me – i can tell you are a joker

Me – [!! - of course not even remotely close to me, i win, hands down in the joker dept..!!!!!!!!!!!!!!!}

Him – I really appologize to u

Him – very sorry

Me – its ok, i guess i was initially put off by your approach

Me – way back when i contacted you a few months ago

Me – and the first thing you said was

Me – "please send a pic"

Him – did u contact me b4?

Me – tonight, i was gasping for water, and by chance you said salaam

Me – wanted to give you a chance and not judge you

Me – yes

Me – i contacted you b4

Me – look at your accepted list

Him – appologize plz… am very sorry….

Me – and read what my initial msg to you was

Me – please there is no need to apologise..

Me – but remember…

Me – what i said..

Me – never make a woman feel that

Him – I dont think I spoke to u b4

Him – I promise

Me – it is only the looks that you are after

Me – you are right we have never spoken

Me – after i got your reply, i was off-put by what you said,

Him – What do u mean

Me – that i didnt bother to pursue

Him – can I tell u something..

Me – go on

Me – but make it quick

Me – i am about to go

Him – I wldnt have contacted u b4 coz I was not open to none gujraati… its only this week I woke and decide to open to muslims from different backgrounds… so since yr profile says Punjabi… I wldnt have contacted u

Him – appologize... but want to tell u

Him – I think u r mistaking me for someone else

Me – believe me i am not

Me – read my msg to you, on the "members who contacted you" list

Me – I believe it will say something like "Next time try having

Me – some sort of conversation first with a woman

Me – anyway, yes i am punjabi, but i am fluent in urdu, degree french and spanish, with basic italian

Me – none of which is relevant to anything

Me – i have to go

Me – thank you for saying hello

Him – sorry if I hurt u

Him – so no friendship?

Me – and i am sure, that you will find that wonderful woman that you seek

Me – you have not hurt me

Me – and i am afraid, no friendship, i do not have male "friends" from this route

Me – nor do i wish to accumulate any during my quest!

Me – as we know what "friends" means when it comes to this

Him– u r SO wonderful... the one who wld have u as a wife... will be lucky

Me – *subhan'Allah*!

Me – what a beautiful thing to say. may He reward you abundantly for saying such a beautiful thing to a total stranger

Me – who is sure that she is not worthy of your kind words

Him – *Ameen*

Me – ok

Me – gotto go,

Him – Pray for me PLEASE

Me – take care

Him – and again APPOLOGIZE

Me – my regards to Naples and that other trouble maker, Patrik

Me – [!!!!!]

Him – :-)

Me – *in sha Allah* i will make *dua* for you,

Him – *Ameen*

Him – u r a NICE person

Me – please say a little prayer for me too

Him – May Allah help you in finding a good husband who can take care of u

Him – and May he grant you the joy of marriage VERY soon

Me – only the One who created me knows me best, but your kind words are graciously accepted,

Me – thank you.

Me – it happens when the time is right

Him – U take care sister in Islam if u rejecting me as friend

Me – do you know that it is His Promise, that

Him – ?

Me – the one who does not find his/her partner in this world, shall be united with them, in the Life yet to come

Him – *Ameen*

Me – so perhaps he waits for me in *Jannah*..

Me – that is why i have to get there

Me – !!!!

Me – ok, enough

Him – *Ameen*!

Him – please make *duas* for me

Him – please

Me – *Allah Malik* [God is King]

Him – please

Him – please

Him – please

Him – u take care my friend...

Me – my *duas* are with all those who come into contact with me..

Him – *Ameen*

Him – u r SO nice

Him – I want to 'explore' more abt u... to c if it can work out

Him – let chat here another day

Me – please i deserve not this kindness, but *subhan'Allah*

Me – i am sorry, i do not have male "friends" from this route

Me – i and i will not be taking this further

Me – in any other form

Him – ok

Him – *Salaams*

Me – must go

Me – *wa-alaikum as-Salaam*

Twenty: Comedy and Tragedy

D ecent enough photo by my side, I took the cyber world by storm. *'Is that really you??'* *'Wow! You look lovely,'* *'That is a gorgeous photo,'* they would say.

It would make me feel good, but sometimes I didn't like the compliments. In fact men gawping at me always made me feel uncomfortable. But, if I was to find a husband, I had to accept that at some point he was going to look at me. With that in mind, I carried on the search with an 'ok-ish' image of myself which came to be voted aesthetically pleasing.

One gentleman contacted me and asked to exchange photographs in the first mail. There wasn't even a *'Hello, how are you?'* It was straight down to business. At first this screamed déjà-vu, but I contained myself because:

a) His profile was well worded. I liked that.
b) He was thirty-five. I liked that too.
c) I could no longer hold on to the previous draconian method when it was plainly obvious that everything boiled down to looks.

With all this in mind, we exchanged photos. He sent me one where he was drowned out by the background. You could hardly see his face. All you could see was the restaurant but I did not complain as I was not concerned with petty image details. What annoyed me though was the message he sent after receiving my photograph, '*Can you send me a colour photo?*' he asked. My photo was still not acceptable. Did it matter that it was a black and white one? Maybe there was no colour in my life? So I mailed him back:

It is not too much to ask for a colour photograph – not at all. In fact I could send you several. I have some very beautiful ones. But if you don't like the way a person looks then the chances are that the colour is not going to make any profound difference.

I understand the need to know what someone looks like [and yes the photograph is not always an accurate depiction of the person] but I want a man who will be quite happy to know the person too, after all the super-ficial will fade but the transcendent will stay, this is perhaps more applicable to women.

I have come across many men, and some have wanted to meet me on the strength of my writing and conversation, without needing to know what I look like. And this has not been because they them-selves are ugly – on the contrary actually. I have some met dynamic men without seeing what they look like and vice-versa. Besides, how would you like it if I had replied to you asking that you send a clearer photograph, one that is more of a close-up, since there is more background than you in the said picture? ... I am not going to because there is no need.

I pray that you find that which you seek.
Nasreen

Dear Nasreen, he wrote back. He said I had given him a big lecture but, the fact remained, that I had sent him, what he described as a 'nebulous' photograph, which of course he said was unlike the very clear one of him that I had been furnished with. He went on to tell me how strange it was that I had many colour photographs yet I chose to send the black and white. He said he didn't know if it was an ideological point I was making, all he knew was that he was just asking for a colour photograph and there was no reason to read anything into what he had asked. Quoting me on the '*But if you don't like the way a person looks then the chances are that the colour is not going to make any profound difference,*' he begged to respectfully disagree.

He continued, saying that if I had asked for a clearer image of him, then he would simply oblige without thinking anything of it. This left me slightly confused. Didn't he maintain that the image he sent was very clear? ... So then why would I need to ask for a clearer image? He carried on saying that he was someone who was direct and honest and was not out to play games or try to score points. Comparing himself to the men I had mentioned, he said that he was in no way as manipulative or as clever as those dynamic men who wanted to give me the impression that they accepted me on the basis of my writings and or conversations.

He ended by telling me that he preferred to write about, contemplate and ponder about issues that really mattered to humanity. Wishing me well, he closed quoting Khalil Jibran, sending his best wishes, hoping that I would find what I was looking for.

I replied:

Thank you for taking the time to write down your thoughts.

Whilst I do not dispute your directness and integrity as a man, the fact remains, irrespective to anything, that you didn't like what I had sent you. Therefore I couldn't see how a colour picture would alter that?

You are clearly a handsome man, which is evident from the very clear photograph I was furnished with, therefore you seek a stunning woman, quite rightly. The ideological point was that perhaps some of us want to be accepted for what we are on the inside also, rather than being immediately judged by the way we look, where ultimately if a person likes the look of you, they will want to talk to you.

Being the regular writer, contemplator and ponderer of humanity that you are, perhaps you will agree that we live in an unfortunately artificial world.

Anyhow, I thank you for your precious time, and am
sure that sooner rather than later, you will find
crystal clear photos, in the way that a clever and
dynamic man will be happy with the very nebulous
me.

The very best of all wishes,
Nasreen

Dear Nasreen, he wrote back. He told me that I had basically
made a great fuss over nothing. He then proceeded to tell me
something that, when things don't go their way, men seem to
love telling women. I am of course referring to the *You Have
Issues* card. He closed sending me kind regards and a Voltaire
quote.

So I wrote back:

Alas, my limited intellectual capacity prevents me
from quoting the great thinkers that have come to
pass this temporary world, but no matter an individual's issues maybe, perhaps we are all lost souls
hoping that someone somewhere will find us? I am
just an ordinary girl with many imperfections and I
am looking for an extraordinary guy who will be
able to see past them.

The problem, sadly for me, is that extraordinary
guys want extraordinary girls. But hope should

never be lost, for it is the essence of that which is yet
to come.

I have thoroughly enjoyed our 'lettres philosophiques'
and I hope you find what you are looking for.

To comedy and tragedy-
Nasreen

Dear Nasreen, he wrote back. He told me that he doubted
very much that I had limited intellect as those who do will
rarely admit. If anything, he said, he considered me to be
smarter than him. He just had more experience that was all.
And, as for perfection, if it was attainable he said, it would not
be worth having.

He told me that he was sorry to disappoint but that he was
not an extraordinary guy in any sense of the word. He then
shared a secret with me and it was this: extraordinary guys
may/not look for extraordinary girls but, he said, extraordinary girls will always look for extraordinary guys. He told me
that these beautiful women were a kind of celebrity who
sought handsome men with six-figure incomes. All over the
globe, he explained, the situation was the same. He knew this
first hand because he told me that he had had plenty of them.
Beauty and sex, he said, could be bought in an instant. Love
cannot be bought because it is priceless.

He described himself as not being the most religious man
on this earth, but every day he took time to thank God for the
beauty of life itself. He told me I was a smart girl and that no

one had seen what tomorrow would bring. Sending me his best wishes, he closed with a Buddha saying.

This encounter was indeed comedy; the way we managed to insult each other very politely. But therein was also the tragedy; that our paths were so similar yet they never got to meet. He was an intelligent man. I like intelligent.

Twenty-one: More Bait

New photograph for a new me. What I now needed was a new profile. Increasingly developing and evolving as a person, I needed to capture this and express what I was searching. So I sat down with my magic pen and the following just flowed:

Someone … to have cheesecake with

Someone to start jobs around the house that will never get finished

Someone to shout at (+ bite-off-head) for no reason

Someone to drag to the same shop at least ten times

Someone to complain to, about annoying people

Someone to be an annoying person to

Someone to blame when things don't go right

Someone to blame when things go wrong

Someone to blame full stop (!!)

Someone to be that shelter from the cold

Someone to live out dreams with

Someone to help triumph over those nasty fears

Someone not afraid to say sorry when sorry

Someone not afraid to forgive upon hearing the sorry

Someone not afraid to admit when lost

Someone not afraid to admit when found

Someone wanting to be found

Someone whose beauty shines brighter with the passing of each moment

Someone whose beauty brings out the beauty in others

Someone to hold during the good bits

Someone to hold onto during the awful ones

Someone to laugh with

Someone to laugh at

Someone to dodge the flying plates

Someone to repair the broken ones

Someone to wipe away the tears

Someone to soak up the hurt

Someone to learn with

Someone to learn from

Someone to learn to … (let's pretend that that makes sense!)

Someone who knows how to pretend that things make sense

Someone to make the knees go weak

Someone with whom to experience the wonders of being human

Someone to pick out names with

Someone to spread lots of goodness with

Someone to journey through the mystery of this temporary world with

Someone … for someone … to give their last rolo to … Forever and ever and ever and ever and ever and ever, to the power of infinity, where the greenbirds nest under the shade of The Magnificent Throne.

Twenty-two: Oceans Apart

'So … come here often?' had been my opening line to him. 'No, but I will from now on!' was the response from this man of few words.

Maybe that is what was interesting about him, attracting me in the first place – his two hundred character profile. That day we were both online and came to exchange a few one-liners. In those days, the sophisticated *Instant Messaging* facility on the matrimonial websites didn't exist, so we relied on internal mail.

Feeling disheartened by the whole search process, when he asked for my number, I just gave it. Usually I was not so quick to give it out and preferred a few deep and meaningful exchanges first, but I realised that my usual approach was not working. We should just meet and get it over with. This was now my thinking.

I was fed up with talking to guys with a backward mindset and I am guilty for assuming that he would be like them. I must've made some awful comments … I didn't need a genius to tell me that I had blown it. He lived in the Home Counties, and was staying over in London with friends. We did politely say that we would meet, but I just thought that it was something to say on his part.

To my amazement, later that night, I did receive a call from him. It was just after 9 p.m. and he said that, by the time he would be free, it would be 11-ish and so meeting was inappropriate but he was calling because he had said that he would call and wanted to fulfil his promise. (Keel over and die not; there are men in this world who actually mean it when they say *'call you later'*). We then agreed to meet that weekend.

The next evening under the pretext of confirming whether we were still on for our rendezvous, I contacted him. Secretly, I wanted to talk to him again, to see how the conversation would be between us. He was on his way back home, and we ended up talking for another few hours. It was nearly 2.30 a.m. when we got off the phone. We were still on for Sunday.

I was unsure about him. Firstly, even though I found him to be humorous he was 'serious' at the same time. Maybe it was me; he was normal and I was the crazy one? After all, I do have a zany sense of humour. Secondly, I have a thing about a man's voice and although his was deep, it hadn't attracted my sense of hearing too much, so I put him down to be just a regular guy.

The day we met, as usual, and as expected, I was late. In my defence, I had warned him that that might be so but I could tell that this annoyed him slightly. But he was quite forgiving, which always helps!

My initial impression was one of mixed feelings. He was indeed handsome but somehow I didn't find him that attractive. We walked to the cafés trying to find somewhere to sit and eat. We must've gone to at least two places before I finally liked one enough to settle upon! I know. I can be unbelievable.

As I sat there and we talked, I watched him. He was so pleasant and had an almost magical aura about him. He was the opposite of what I thought he would be. I have met many *wannabe* professional men, but this guy … he really was something unique: a true gentleman, well spoken, intelligent and warm. The more I looked at him, the more I realised how extremely good-looking he was.

Varsha would really love you, I thought to myself.

She always talked about how a man with chiselled features did it for her. I was not really into that; maybe because I hadn't come across any handsome 'chiselled' guys. I had to lower my gaze and I am sure that he mistook it for the fact that I was being rude but I knew that if I kept looking at him, my eyes would explode … he was so magnetic . . .

We talked and it was comfortable. I spoke a little about my life, as did he. He said he had a turbulent relationship with his brother and it had reached a point where it was straining the rest of the family. Also his parents were now beginning to worry that at thirty-five years of age, their younger son was no closer to marriage. He talked about a possible move abroad, which had been on the cards for many months.

We went to pray at Regent's Park *masjid* and talked further in the car. Suddenly, it hit me; this guy sitting next to me was actually extremely handsome … more than I had attributed him to be. He was the classic good-looking man that every woman would die for. I had never met or even seen anyone like him before. He was just 'wow'.

The other striking thing about him was that he seemed so *shareef* [decent] and 'nice'. In my twisted world that would automatically mean that he would probably be *boring*, whereas my 'type', up to that point, had been the '*player*'. We talked and joked about the player thing. In my profile I mentioned that I was not looking for that type of man. When he asked me what sort of guy I was looking for, I confessed that the player was attractive and I hoped to come across a decent ... player. (Forgive me, I don't make sense sometimes!)

We arranged to meet outside after prayers and he dropped me back to my car. We didn't mention anything about meeting again or calling each other as you do upon parting with someone. I didn't want polite *farewells* and *so longs*; he was a stunning human being and probably wanted someone equally stunning, so he would never be interested in me. Besides, I was not a high-flying professional woman to match his social standing so I probably didn't stand a chance. I knew I wouldn't hear from him again and neither had I wanted to see him: I just wanted to leave with the memory of a wonderful encounter with an honourable gentleman.

A few hours later, I received a text message to see if I had got home ok. I was taken aback by this gesture. I really did not expect to hear from him again. If nothing else, then this man had just won the 'sincerity' tick. A man who checks to see if I have got home after seeing him always earns a gold star in my book.

I messaged back trying to be pleasant, at the back of my mind thinking that he was just being polite. Then he rang and we talked. I didn't think that we would talk so soon. He told me that he had found me to be intelligent (which was nice to hear!) but quieter in person than I had been on the phone. The truth was that I had been intimidated by him. Many would be, understandably ...

The conversation just flowed and I waited for the right moment to tell him that I didn't think that we were suited to each other because we came from two different worlds; I could never compete with what he was used to. Also, I had felt no 'pull' towards him as you do when in the company of someone of the opposite sex. Surely this was an indication that he '*didn't do it for me*'.

As we were talking his two-year-old nephew, Subhan, who was staying at their house, began to get in his uncle's way.

'One moment please,' he said, as he moved the phone away to scold his nephew.

'*Behteh, pyjama kidder hai?*' [Where are your bottoms?] he asked his mischievous little nephew who was running around without his pyjamas.

'Now he is sticking his tongue out as if to say, *what are you going to do about it!*' he told me.

He sounded heavenly from the moment he said '*behteh*', a term of affection used to refer to the young, that I swear my heart did a few somersaults ... I couldn't understand it though. A man speaking Urdu never attracted me but just then, from that very millisecond, the voice thing fell into place. A shiver rushed down my spine and I felt drawn into a state of enchantment ... His voice had somehow deepened and I wanted to see him, again, that very moment ... I don't know why but I just did.

We spoke a few times after that and the text messages were constant, unlike our conversations. Often there were spouts of silence and I felt that I needed to fill in the gaps. There was no element of flirting or sexual connotation; it was clean and I respected him so much for that. This was the first time ever since my search had started that a man had been respectful towards me. So far even the *religious* ones I had come across hadn't been able to resist, but this man ... He was an outstanding beacon of reverence. The more I spoke with him, the more elevated he became in my eyes.

I did find him to be quite reserved though, not giving much away, and I didn't know what to make of that. One night we were talking about accents and voice and I talked about how his slight accent was quite off-putting. I harped on about it a bit too much, so that in the end he told me that he would go, taking his accent with him. He then hung up.

It was official; I was the Queen of *Foot in Mouth* (I lecture on most days, if anyone wants any tips on how to totally blow your chances with a guy).

I did text to apologise. And I told him that if it had bothered me that much, I wouldn't talk to him. I rang him the next day and left a message on his phone. I emailed him too, because I am a psychopath like that.

He texted me that night and we started talking again. Over the next few weeks, we spoke occasionally, but he seemed to have a lot on his mind. In the days that followed, I didn't hear from him. I presumed that he needed space to be alone away from me. I felt that I was imposing on him during his difficult time, and I didn't want to do that.

Then came a long weekend, a friend was going through a rough patch in her relationship and she had asked if I would go and stay with her in Birmingham. I returned on the Monday, having spent most of the weekend nursing her broken heart and soaking up her tears, so I hadn't slept at all. Arriving home exhausted beyond belief, having nearly grabbed forty winks at the wheel during my drive back, I had just opened the front door, put my bags down, did *wudhu* [ablution in preparation for prayer], was about to pray, when I received a phone call. It was him.

He was on his way to Nottingham to see his best friend who had agreed to sell his car for him, so he needed to drop the car off and get back to London that same night. It was already nearly 8 p.m. He rang because he was stopping off to offer *Maghrib* [sunset prayer] and there was something he needed to tell me. It was sheer coincidence that he was just passing my way, and I asked if he wanted to meet. We agreed to meet briefly as he had to get going.

'Whereabouts are you?'

'I have just passed Office World,' he replied.

I was a few hundred yards from Office World! He would be at my house in less than three minutes! Before I hung up the phone, he was there!

He parked outside and I was so excited that in the frenzy of it all, I totally forgot to fix myself up! I just didn't think … I wanted to see him … so badly, I had forgotten what he looked like! I had gone from not being interested in him, to kind of falling for this man, and I had Subhan to thank for that! … I didn't care if he was neat and nice or whether he came from a background I could never reach; I just couldn't wait to see him. And I did.

... Oh, did I see him ...

... At that particular moment in time, I understood what '*dying and going to heaven*' had meant ... He looked gorgeous, like a vision from above ... As if carved by Angels ...

He was wearing suave glasses, and looked quite rough; hadn't shaved for a few days so his gorgeous face was characterised by grey stubble (oh, yes please!). He was wearing a casual top and had biceps that you want wrapped around you ... I am certain I didn't breathe for a few seconds because I just couldn't!

This was my type! The first time I had seen him he was just normal. But this was sexy, passionate, masculine ... oh yes! As he walked towards me, I could hear the beat of my heart and hoped that he couldn't ...

'I like your shoes,' he said with a smirk.

I looked down at my feet and saw my slippers – the *cow with a daisy in its mouth* motif just staring at me so innocently! I had forgotten to change my slippers! How embarrassing!

We talked and he said that he wanted to tell me a few nights earlier that he was leaving ... for Perth ... but Subhan, who had been drinking his bottle of milk while in his uncle's arms, had made too much noise and hadn't let him talk.

He was now on his way to Manchester to sell his car, and pick up his best friend. The flight was in a few days, and he hadn't wanted to leave without telling me ...

…What?????… WHAT??…You are leaving!!

'… You are never coming back?' I whispered softly.

He looked at me, and smiled, sighing with frustration.

We just stood there. I couldn't believe that he was going. I lied and told him that if that is what he wanted, then I was happy for him. I wasn't happy at all. He said it was not out of want but out of necessity. He had an open ticket, for a month, but wasn't sure whether it would be longer, shorter or never. He didn't know what was happening. All he knew was that he was leaving. I didn't know what to say to him. He couldn't leave just like that. It was all too much to take in. And he was late for prayer.

I told him to go and pray but to drop by the house after he had finished. We couldn't leave it just like that. I didn't care if anyone saw him coming to my house (and then reporting it on the national news) – nothing seemed to matter anymore.

After he had been to the *masjid*, he parked up and rang me. I went to meet him, and he came into the house. Just my luck, my sisters had come around by then too. They usually come around but that day they hadn't and it had been just me and my brother at home. All day we had spent alone. But all of a sudden, my sisters had invaded the house. (Fate: it strikes you when you are not looking ... be warned!)

He greeted my sisters as he came in; one was in the middle of telling her little boy off and I don't think she acknowledged it; the other was so shocked to see such a gorgeous man in our house that she just froze. To be honest, I didn't want to introduce them to him; I was too embarrassed. Families go out of their way to ruin our lives; why?

Recovering from this slight death, we sat in my front room.

'You have the *player* look today!' I joked.

'That will teach me to not listen to my mother,' he said. 'She says you should never be scruffy, as you never know what will happen.'

I am glad he hadn't listened to his mother that day. The *ruffed* up look suited him tremendously!

My brother was on his way out and I introduced them. He talked about going to Perth, initially as a one month long break, but if job opportunities arose then he would consider them. He had already had a few interviews. I sat there watching this gorgeous man, sitting on my sofa; did I see my children in his eyes? ...

When my brother left, he told me that he didn't want to leave like this with things so bad between him and his family. And that he was bringing his best friend back with him that night, to help reach some kind of reconciliation before he left. I could feel his pain but I didn't want to make too much fuss.

After he had gone you can imagine the whole house was buzzing with 'Who *was* that *gorgeous* man?' Even my six-year-old niece asked me who that nice man was. I tried telling her that he was their uncle's friend, and that I knew him as well, to which the six-year-old giggled and said, 'No … don't lie … he was *your* boyfriend!' (… Oh I wish, I wish!)

That night I didn't want to call him. He seemed upset, and I knew that talking was probably the last thing on his mind. Especially to me, a total stranger, who practically knew nothing of the situation. And I didn't want him to feel awkward. It was obvious that he had things to sort out. So I texted him and told him that I had a headache.

I left him alone for a while. Surely he couldn't still be interested in me after my no make-up, sisters' behaviour and cow slippers … We did have a text message exchange on the eve of his departure.

'The women in Australia, they are not all called Anna are they?' I asked.

'No. You are thinking of Polish women,' he replied.

(When we first met, we talked about the time he spent in Poland and how Polish women were highly beautiful. I had a flatmate who was Polish, Anna, and we laughed at how almost all Polish women were called *Anna*).

'Well, you never know, they might all have moved to Australia by the time you get there!'

'I hope not.'

'If I was you, I would be more worried about all those poisonous spiders though.'

'That's the least of my worries.'

'Oh? What is the greatest?'

'As the saying goes: dying is easy it's the living that scares me to death.'

'I remember when I wanted to go and live in Spain,' I replied. 'I realised that I didn't need to go thousands of miles away to know that I was so alone.'

'It's not to realise the loneliness. It's to legitimise it.'

It was time for prayer, so I had to go. I told him to get his prayer done too, and call me when he had finished. He couldn't leave without saying goodbye.

'Say goodbye,' was his message.

I was totally useless at goodbyes, but I threw a few words together with the hope that 'goodbye' would not mean *goodbye*.

'Ok. Thanks. Bye,' he texted back.

'No great speech?'

'Not into speeches … just as useless at goodbyes.'

Disappointed, I rang him. He seemed down, upset, hurt; if only I could do something for him? We talked for well over an hour without making any progress. He was leaving my life and I didn't want him to. But I didn't want to tell him either. Varsha always told me that I needed to be more reserved, that maybe my upfront approach put these men off.

'Play your cards a little nearer to yourself,' she would say.

I didn't know how to. However so far, I hadn't been bold with this man and was trying to just *go with the flow* (whatever 'the flow' actually is). Of course, during this time, Varsha had decided that she needed to go backpacking around the world and, heartlessly, she left me to fend for myself. So while all this was going on, she knew nothing. And all I knew was that I had been exercising her advice without much success; he was leaving my life and I didn't want him to.

'Can I read you a poem?' he asked suddenly. He was packing and the book was on his desk.

'Please,' I answered.

'It's by Shelley,' and he continued:

The fountains mingle with the river
And the rivers with the ocean,
The winds of heaven mix for ever
With a sweet emotion;
Nothing in the world is single,
All things by a law divine
In one another's being mingle—
Why not I with thine?

See the mountains kiss high heaven,
And the waves clasp one another;
No sister-flower would be forgiven
If it disdain'd its brother;
And the sunlight clasps the earth,
And the moonbeams kiss the sea—
What are all these kissings worth,
If thou kiss not me?'

My heart silently cried as I knew I didn't want this to be goodbye.

'Don't go. Stay. Stay with me,' I told him, not being able to hold back any longer.

I was so confused. One minute he is reading me poems, the next he is telling me that he doesn't want me to put my life on hold. That he wants me to move on, that he doesn't know what he is going to do or what is going to happen and that he doesn't want to make me promises that he cannot fulfil.

I told him to be straight with me; if he wasn't interested, then that was ok, but to be honest. He said that I was getting the wrong idea, and what he was saying was for the best. I could only assume that he didn't want to know and I needed to carry on with my search if that was the case. I had even told someone that I couldn't speak with him (You read about him in Chapter Seventeen: *Inspired By* ...). He told me that I should do what I had to.

I realised that it was no use. Clearly, he was not interested. I had asked if he would call me from Australia, and he had said that I shouldn't hold my breath. I told him that I had started writing an email, which I had, and that if I sent it then would he read it? He said he would but that he couldn't guarantee that I would receive a reply. I asked why he didn't want to maintain contact with me, if I had grasped the wrong end of the stick, like he had said. His reply was that he was running away from everything to do with England; the country and the people.

'I need to get away from here, as far as possible,' he said.

In the end I admitted defeat, wished him well and that was it.

The next day, I hoped that it would have gone away. The night before had been a difficult one; I wondered if I would be able to get through it. How much more would my poor heart be able to take? I shouldn't cry though; surely I must have known that it was too good to be true and that it wouldn't happen, not to me? I tried to get rid of the thoughts in my head but it wasn't working. *'What are all these kissings worth, if thou kiss not me?'* … this wouldn't go away.

I needed to find that Shelley poem. I needed to see those words that he had read out to me. I didn't know what the poem was called, or which year it had been written, all I knew was that it was by Shelley and that those were the last two lines. I needed to see those words; touch them. I needed to know what it was that he was trying to tell me the night before.

I went off to the library and spent all day trying to track down that poem. You can imagine what a task that was: Shelley wrote a lot of poems in his lifetime! It was like searching for a needle in a haystack. I searched all those works by Shelley, and books that had been written about Shelley, in the hope that I would find it. It was imperative that I find that poem.

When I eventually did, a single tear came to my eye … The poem was called *'Love's Philosophy'*. Seeing it just pulled the strings of my heart and it hurt enormously. He was gone so far away and that hurt. I couldn't understand. I knew that he was a total stranger and that it was just one of those things that people walk in and out of our lives every day, but this was different. I had to bring him back.

I emailed him but there was no reply. *'My house was probably not big enough for him,'* I remember telling a friend. He really had gone. He had left my life, pretty much in the same way that he had entered it. So life had to carry on. My search had to carry on and I tried to continue … but it was no use. I couldn't stop thinking about him. So I bowed out graciously and took a break.

When I went back to the search, I contacted a whole host of eligible bachelors. Time had gone by and I hadn't received a reply from two who were undecided. I wanted my list to be clear; if they weren't interested, then fine, at least I could delete them and move on; if they wanted to accept, then they should so that we could talk. That is the attitude I developed.

One declined and one of them accepted. Although the latter might as well have declined too as he was quite appalling at communicating. I think we must have exchanged one message, and I never heard from him again for another month, when I think I got a few words out of him. I replied sending some details about myself. I didn't hear anything.

Six weeks later, he replied. I told him that I had given up on hearing from him. By this time, I was tired of the whole charade of looking. I decided that he would be the last person that I would talk to. After that I would be putting the laptop to rest. I added him to my messenger list but we never did catch each other online.

Another month went by and *Ramadhan*, the Muslim month of fasting, started. Early one morning, at about 6a.m., I was doing some work and we caught each other on messenger. He said 'hi', and we talked. Gradually, these conversations became frequent. It was always early mornings, as straight after fasting

I wasn't sleeping, but instead having early nights and early mornings. One morning he was telling me how it had thundered all night the night previously and that it was monsoon season in Perth...

Oh Lord! It was him ... I thought that it may have been him at the beginning because he was bad at keeping in touch, but then I didn't want to assume; the profile was different as was the username. In the past I have always been so convinced about people, certain almost only to find out that they really weren't who I thought they were! If there had been any doubts, then there weren't any now. But I didn't say anything and another few months went by like this.

'Rehana, he knows it's me,' I said to a close friend.

'How do you know?' she asked.

'He hasn't asked me my name. That's the first thing people ask, right? And he hasn't.'

I hadn't asked him because by then I knew who he was. But he didn't know who I was; I had changed my user ID, my profile was different, the email was different; so why hadn't he asked me what my name was?

It was now December 2004 and the world would witness probably the worst natural disaster mankind has ever seen. On Boxing Day, the tsunami hit South Asia. Of course, like everyone, I was so overcome with feelings of disbelief and fear that it was unbearable. Days later, I saw the newspaper lying around and there was a map of the affected areas; that is when it registered. I cannot describe what went through my mind, when I saw the red rings labelled '*worst hit*' on the map around Indonesia. He was supposed to be there that weekend for a friend's wedding. What if he had been near the coast when the tidal wave struck? I think I lost sensation in my body for a few moments: I needed to know that he was ok. Please God, this couldn't be happening.

I didn't have a telephone number. I didn't even know his last name. All I had was a lousy email address. I was so worried. I sent him a message via messenger. But I didn't hear anything. That time was one of severe agony; I was helpless. Eventually, a message did arrive telling me that he was ok.

Soon New Year's Day dawned upon us and I had to make an 'executive decision'. All our correspondence had taken place as if he didn't know who I was. What would I do if, out of the blue, he asked me what my name was? If he knew my identity, maybe he wouldn't want to communicate with me? So I sent him a New Year's message; I changed my email address and gave him the option of staying in touch. In that message, I also went on to reveal my name. If he still wanted to stay in contact, then that would be great and I could stop running. If not, then I could say goodbye with the old year and look forward to a brand new fresh one having let go of the past.

Relieved that he added my new address to his list, I was also uncertain how to approach this. Suddenly becoming inundated with work did not help matters but it provided the perfect excuse for my cowardice and it meant that I could avoid or at least delay the rejection that I feared from him. Luckily for me, the routine that I had adopted during *Ramadhan* now wore off. I was no longer getting early nights and early mornings, so we no longer caught each other online.

But this didn't mean that I didn't know when he was online. I must confess, I used to deliberately leave my machine switched on all the time, so that I could hear him as he logged on. Knowing that he was on the other end of the laptop was such a comfort. I could feel his presence, as if he was here, right beside me. Sometimes I would be fast asleep but then, when he logged onto messenger, it made that knocking sound as if on a door and that alert would wake me up. I would smile as I opened my eyes but stay in bed until I went back to sleep minutes later. It brought much satisfaction to my soul to hear him knocking as if on my heart … waking emotions that I had come to feel for him. This gave me a warm feeling inside and I felt safe; as if a sincere love was being born …

We had been talking for well over three months like this. He was over there, and I was over here; oceans apart. I didn't think that it would go anywhere, and if it would, then the direction seemed unclear. I think that perhaps deep down somewhere he was thinking the same sort of thing. Because six weeks later, when I finally logged on, we spoke, and that night he told me that he had known all along who I was …

Of course! How stupid of me; the first line of my profile:

'Someone to have cheesecake with'

He knew how much I loved cheesecake. In fact the first time we met, when we were playing musical chairs in the restaurants, the reason was that none of them were selling cheesecakes.

'How badly do you want the cheesecake?' he asked.

'Extremely,' I replied.

And so we just hopped from one place to another, until out of sheer embarrassment we finally decided to stay in the one in which we were standing! Actually, I went back to that restaurant a few times, and just stood outside, by the window, content at staring at the table where we had sat; imagining us sitting there, having that conversation. It's as if I am watching a couple sitting there; a scene from a movie and I, a member of the audience. I am sure the restaurant owners think I am weird. That, or they need to look into getting some sort of restraining order as I just stand there, looking into their restaurant, the inner me just smiling, and then I walk away.

But that night when he told me that he had known all along, it was a breath of fresh air; an out of this world experience. It was 3 a.m., UK time, and it had just started to snow. It was the first sign of the break of early spring and there was an inexplicable charm in the air. It was probably a most romantic moment of my life even though I was alone. But I didn't feel alone. As the pure snow gently fell from the peaceful pre-dawn sky, I felt a new awakening from within.

One morning, he came online and told me that a few nights previously, he had fallen severely ill. It broke my heart to hear this. All I wanted was to take care of him and all he had to do was to just say; I would drop everything and go be with him. But he just wouldn't open up and let me in.

Even though he denied it, I knew that he was still yearning for a lost love. I once said to him that you know that someone is for you if you can see your children in their eyes. He told me that once he had seen his grandchildren in someone's eyes. It became obvious the more we spoke. The reason why I could relate to him was because, like me, he too had been in a triangle. Sadly, when there are three people involved, one will always be scathed. I wanted to help him through it, and even if he wasn't interested in me, I felt that having experienced something similar, I could make a difference in some way so that, in time, he would be able to open his heart to someone, even if that someone was not me.

I thought about him constantly. I remember one morning I had had problems with my laptop; the connection lead died on me but I desperately needed to know if he was any better. It was snowing heavily (good old British weather; snow in spring!) that morning and schools were closed. My car wouldn't start so I trekked on foot, all the way to my sister's house just so that I could use her computer and see if he was ok.

However, I didn't know where I stood with him. Were we friends? Was he interested in me? Where would it all lead? Would it go anywhere? Was it a wise thing to do, to be in this situation, if he didn't want to be with me, knowing that I was setting myself up for more hurt? Many times I wanted to ask him, but I was scared that he would stop talking to me, and I wanted him to talk to me more than him not talking to me! Then one morning, it just happened.

'You told me about someone for my friend?' he asked. 'Some guy, what was his ID again?'

Someone had contacted Shanaz, but she was no longer looking and so we added him to our *personal database* ready for someone suitable to come along.

'Is he no good for you?' he asked.

'Seems I am no good for anybody.'

'I am sure you are good for somebody.'

'Yes, but does that somebody know it?'

'You seem to fill the criteria, so what is the problem?' he continued.

'I don't know. I am obviously going wrong somewhere.'

'Then that is a question mark on your personality; you have to be more positive. That is where you are going wrong,' he replied. 'You have to believe that you are loveable, and that many can love you. Once you radiate that ... it will shine through. Positivity breeds confidence, which breeds self assurance. Once you have that, no one can resist you.'

'I don't lack in the confidence dept. And I don't want to be loved by many; just the one ...'

'Well one will come from many.'

'He will?'

'Yes.'

'I have been looking properly since I was twenty-seven. I have met many. But that doesn't mean I want to be loved by all, in the hope that one will come along.'

'That's not my point,' he protested.

'The thing is if you are honest with men, they run. Why do you guys do that?'

'Well ... depends what you are being honest about!'

'I can't figure out all this dating thing. Besides, the online matrimonial search is practically cyber dating whether a person admits it or not.'

'I am not sure what you mean but anyway I—'

'I mean what is a woman to do,' I interrupted. 'How does it work? You put up a profile, with your specifics, someone replies or you may find them and then what?'

'Then if the two of you hit it off … as you get to know each other … it progresses. And once you both are at a stage where you think it can work … and both have the guts … you go for it.'

'Ah … see it's just that; what is *getting to know each other?*'

'Oh come on!'

'No seriously.'

'It means expending time and energy; finding out things about one another; see what kind of thought patterns the other person has.'

'Ah yes, time and energy; something you don't have to devote to the search! I remember.'

'We are not talking about me here, we are talking about you.'

'Well I am not very good at this; I thought that when you know that you are interested in someone, you should tell them.'

'Well that does help,' he laughed.

'Only sometimes it does not,' I continued, 'So tell me how long have you been looking?'

'On and off … a few years now.'

'And have there been many that you have been interested in?'

'A few.'

'So why didn't you pursue? Couldn't have been that interesting?'

'No, maybe the other side was not interested,' he replied.

'That is what I am trying to tell you; it doesn't matter if you are oozing in confidence; most often the one you want doesn't want you.'

'Beside the point,' he argued. 'Unless you ooze in confidence, there won't even be a start. Those others may not have been interested in my inquiry but there are also many who have shown interest and I have not .... So it balances out ...'

'So it's a no-win situation?'

'Well there you go ... that's the difference between an optimist and a pessimist; I see it as a win-win situation.'

'We are so very different then or maybe you just don't understand me. Perhaps you don't want to?'

'I guess, maybe, what does it matter?'

'Exactly. I am just a name on a messenger list; just words on a screen for you,' I replied.

'... ah ... hello ...'

'Hi'

'That sounds a little unfair.'

'On the contrary,' I retaliated. 'If something happened to me, and I never came on here again, it won't make a difference to you, I know that now.'

'I guess you have the right to your opinions, but it hurts to hear that.'

'It hurts to say that, you don't know much,' I told him.

'We may not be close friends, and I may be 10,000 miles away, but I thought I merited a little more. Obviously I was way off the mark,' he replied.

'Trust me you are not. But I was thinking, recently, I wrote you an email. Remember on the eve of my birthday, I dreamt of you? I thought about you so much that day you talked about love; it deeply affected me and I wrote an email. But I was scared to send you it. And I realised many things. And even if you had been right here, you would still be 10,000 miles away; so like a coward I didn't send it to you.'

'Ok and the point being …?'

'The point being that, I realised that at the end of the day, I was nothing more than just a name on a screen and that tomorrow you could find somebody and that's it,' I replied with an internal sadness.

'Of course that is mutual; it can be exactly the same for you,' he said.

'… My GOD! Don't you see?? I am here; I am not interested in anyone but you. There I said it and I am not sorry I said it.'

'Now you blur the boundary lines,' he said.

'There were no boundary lines. I mean for crying out aloud, where was I when I came across you? On a website for a reason; not to make friends, or have a laugh. I can understand people's reasons for being cautious, but sometimes there are some genuine people out there; that is why it hurts, when you talk about being alone and all that and I think why can't you love me? I don't have any hidden agendas and it gets too much and I realised that in that email it was obvious that I was asking you to let me love you (again) and come on how many times can a girl do that?! But you look everywhere else, everywhere but at the name on your messenger list. And I don't care how all this sounds but it needed to be said and I appreciate that I may have blown you away with that so, um ... I can call you an ambulance?' I laughed.

'Have you finished?'

'For now yes. But I can go on, if you like? Duracell you know.'

'I am sure you can,' he laughed. 'But I think it's enough for today; remember you were burning the midnight oil for reasons other than this.'

Little did he know that I would've burnt the oil in every lantern if it meant that he could tell me what my heart yearned to hear.

'Call me an ambulance please!'

'I will but they will have to attend to me first. I still haven't recovered from the shock of finding out that it was you all along! And that wasn't bad enough; it hurts me when you are on that site talking to others. I can't explain it because you are a free agent after all but ... some things are out of my control.'

'I can't get a word in edgeways today ...'

'No. No you can't. Because I don't want to hear, *I don't feel the same about you* or worse; silence. So ... I am going to force myself on you!'

'I shall keep silent,' he said.

'No! Don't. That is irritating. Say something (but not that which you are not allowed to say!),' and we both laughed.

'I am glad that the fact that I am sitting here with my heart in my hands is a means of entertainment for you,' I said eventually. 'We live in a most cruel world.'

'Indeed we do,' he replied. 'Me and my big mouth about being confident and self-assured ... I take it all back!' and then we had another giggle.

'On a slightly serious note ...' he continued, 'I thought our friendship came about because we had moved on from the *site* issues ...'

'Of course, but I couldn't go on without telling you this. I have wanted to but I was scared. I didn't expect that you would still be here.'

'But that's so unfair,' he said. 'But then again what do you care? When has a woman ever cared about being fair?'

'Ah! You see this is it; you have got to let me show you that not all are the same. I am not trying to take anyone else's place; just make a bit of room for me. Everything I have ever said to you has been sincere; straight from the heart. Sometimes you just got to take a chance.'

'But you do realise you are being extremely unfair still?'

'I am sorry; how?'

'By saying what you have said etc.'

'Why is that unfair?'

'Just because you have quickly passed over my remark about being unfair does not mean you are not unfair.'

'Ok, tell me why am I unfair? I don't want to be.'

'You agreed yourself that you were being unfair.'

'Are you just naturally difficult or are you really doing your best to be?' I asked him.

'Uff! Never mind,' he said perhaps realising that he was being unfair!

'I think our friendship came along because I assumed that you wouldn't be here; that you weren't interested,' I carried on.

'But then how could we have been friends if I was not *here?*'

'You know what I mean; once I knew who you were, I thought that if you knew who I was, I would never hear from you again.'

'Ummmm ... ok ... that is really making sense now ...??&*^%$#@'

'I am sure you will figure it out; that is if you want to.'

'Sure ... another classic escape line from a woman.'

'And what was all that earlier on about *pessimism?* ... like, hello??'

'Hi!' he replied.

'I don't like to have escape lines.'

'But you do,' he protested.

'With things that matter; I guess it's dependent on the situation. But I can tell you I don't here. I have nothing to run away from. I am not afraid any more.'

'That's more like it,' he responded.

'I have just bared my soul to you.'

'Do you feel lighter for it; getting it off your chest?'

'I do actually, yes.'

'Great!'

'I like to know where I stand. Look, I can't offer you status or anything grand, you already know that.'

'Shhh ...' he said.

'No please let me say it, I am on a roll here!'

'You are leaning towards 'insulting me' now—'

'I guess that would be unfair,' I interrupted.

'… Like your other *unfairs*,' he added cheekily.

'If you knew anything about me …'

'Yes well that is it; I don't know anything about you. You won't let me into your world.'

'No I won't. And there are reasons for that.'

'That says it all then,' I said dispirited.

'And you know them … we are all fighting our little battles here …'

'You don't have to.'

'I have my own cross to carry and it feels pretty heavy when your family won't speak to you … and you can't do anything about it, anyway I hope that I have interrupted your *roll*.'

'Do you think that someone can love you one day?' I asked curiously.

'What!' he exclaimed. 'I can be loved any day!' and then we laughed once more.

'I don't think you want to be loved.'

'Ok.'

'Maybe just not by me,' I said.

'Whatever you say,' he replied.

'You know sometimes, when the opportunity comes your way, you shouldn't shy away from it.'

'You have to be in a position to not shy away from it,' he pointed out.

'Why are you not in a position to love or be loved?'

'Because I am in the office, working!'

'You will be in the position when you want to be,' I reminded him with a more serious tone.

'Yes,' he agreed. 'Sure. I am so happy to see you turn into an optimist. All this has been worth it.'

'Buried optimism.'

'It's a start,' he replied.

'I bare my soul often to people who don't want to know. It comes naturally.'

'How would I know …?' he asked.

'I don't know …' I replied. 'But fancy that hey …'

'Exactly.'

'How stupid would that be …?'

'On a scale from one to ten …' and with that we both chuckled.

'Not that it made a difference,' I reminded him.

By now it was time for *Fajr* [dawn prayer] and I had to go. We must've spent over four hours online.

'Apologies for keeping you,' he said. 'Forgive me, I didn't know it was *Fajr* already.'

'It's ok, you didn't.'

'Of course, I knew that!'

I really wanted to tell him a quick story but he said that I had three minutes to tell him because he wanted me to go and pray.

'You know how I can't tell stories quickly!'

'Ok then save it for another day, pray and then get some rest.'

'*In sha Allah,*' I said. 'And I hope you recover from the slight bump on the head!'

'*In sha Allah,*' he replied. 'I hope you do too!'

We did speak after this conversation a few times and he started opening up to me. I remember telling Rehana how different it was beginning to feel. He was making more of a concerted effort to give me an insight into his world and to get to know mine. He spoke of his family and his friends, something which he hadn't done before.

'My friend from Hong Kong is here,' he told me one morning. 'So we are going for a *bhelpuri* [Indian appetiser] … and gonna spend the whole evening together going around town … a bit like …*Before Sunrise.*'

'I have never seen that film. Who is in it?' I asked.

'If I have to tell you then it doesn't really matter at all … It's an old film. Never mind.'

'No, not that old … It rings a bell; but not loud enough … It's something to do with Ethan Hawke? I think it's on my list of films I need to watch.'

'Yep; that's the one. Anyway he meets a strange girl and they spend the whole evening together in Rome and in the morning they part. But in that one evening it could have been a lifetime etc. etc. So I was just teasing my friend—'

'Threatening that you will fall in love with her?'

'No. Even worse; that we would spend the night together and tomorrow I will disappear!'

'That is normal for men, I am sure.'

'Not really. Not for me anyway.'

'That is good.'

'I usually disappear after two days …' he laughed. 'I think you been hanging round the wrong type of men,' he added.

'Yes, but you get to experience something before your disappearance right?'

'Hmmm … anyway …'

'I hope you have a good weekend … hey maybe you can throw a barbie on the barbie,' I suggested and then we broke into fits of laughter.

It was going well, and he made final arrangements to come back to the UK for a few days. I didn't ask to see him, not that I didn't want to because I really did, so much, but I was afraid he would turn me down. He didn't suggest meeting either, so I just let it be.

Things were never the same after that as I hesitated going online. It was becoming difficult as my confession to him had made no positive difference but instead made it awkward. I was back to the *not knowing* stage and I hated the uneasy feeling that that brought. I needed to know where I stood, if anywhere; but I was too afraid to hear those words, '*You're a nice girl … but …*'

His birthday crept up, and I sent him an e-card to which I didn't get any sort of response. This was a shame as it was a most beautiful card, inviting him to pick a star and make a wish and asking who would want candles when the starry sky was there for the taking.

'Happy Birthday right up to Before Sunset …'

This was my message to him … In the way that I had known that he was talking about me and him with his reference to *Before Sunrise*.

Sadly for me, although in the films, Jesse and Celine would get a second chance, we would not. Weeks later, I caught him on messenger a few times, and when I went to say hello, he would log out. Upset by this, I knew only one thing remained.

Just to let you know that I will no longer be logging into messenger using that account, so you don't need to worry any more about feeling awkward and logging off when I come online. I never wanted to make you uncomfortable and I am sorry that I seem to have done exactly that. Please know that that was never my intention.

I do hope sincerely that sooner rather than later, you will come across a woman for whom you will want to let down your barriers (or even miss that plane …)

To love someone and be loved back must be a wonderful thing. Perhaps you know already and perhaps I will find out one day.

Nasreen

I hope, if he hasn't already, that he finds a marvellous woman who can love him truly with all her heart and appreciate what a distinguished gentleman he is. More than that, I wish for him the spark to want to love. Maybe I got it wrong; maybe that spark was there and had been all along, but that unfortunately, it just wasn't for me?

He replied back weeks later saying that there was a problem with his messenger, and that every time he went to reply, it would log him out. It has been years since this happened, and well … if he had really wanted to, he could've had it fixed by now.

'You send me letters of love, on the moon,' the night said to the sun, '… and I leave you my reply as tears upon the grass.'

Sometimes I wonder if Tagore wrote these words especially for me.

Twenty-three: Final Bait

By now my search had become painful and highly frustrating. Deep down I felt that fate wasn't on my side but I couldn't give up hope. I knew what I wanted and what I had to offer. Surely there was one man on this earth who wanted to be with me?

Well I had to find him.
Whoever he was …
Wherever he was …

And so, with my *toujours fidel* pen, the following profile was born:

No fantastic opening lines. No flamboyant adjectives to describe myself. No lies to tell about how friends think I am great (they probably hate me). No interest in caste or such absurd nonsense. No hunger for materialism. No great love of/for traditional culture. No keeping up appearances. No claims of going to the gym. No foreign stamps on my passport. No claim to fame. No competitor of societal wants. No sense of humour on certain days of the month (guaranteed). No time for those who are miserly with theirs. No respect for those who lack compassion. No need for people who have extreme difficulty in thinking about others. No attraction to that which lacks power. No greater aphrodisiac than intelligence.

No players who use matrimonial websites as a serious pastime. No deluded individuals who think that if you throw a casual in sha Allah/ma sha Allah & Salaam, then that means you are 'religious'. No ignoramuses who think that a spiritual woman cannot be or indeed should not be a progressive thinker. No men who don't know what they want. No weak-hearted folk. No men who feel compelled to reply to adverts on the basis of the 'very fair' option. No (un)tactful diplomats who don't know how to ask a woman if she has had a previous relationship. No shallow freaks who want a stunning woman and yet are nothing to look at themselves (yes, stunning woman also seeks breathtakingly gorgeous man so, if you are, then it might be worth stepping this way. And if you are not, then it still might be worth stepping this way).

Simply: Looking for the one who is looking for me.

Twenty-four: Mr No

'I am literally on for a few moments, but I saw your profile and it left me shouting from the rooftops.' He was just logging off and asked if I would be around later that night.

'I am, but *betrothed* at 10.30!' I replied.

'Well, I will come and seek you when you are free,' he pledged. 'Late is better for me as I won't be around tomorrow and I really wanted to speak with you. But if you marry that 10.30 guy, then I will be gutted!' he laughed and then logged off.

I waited for him later that evening but he did not show up. I was left a little disappointed; he had seemed genuine, and his words sounded sincere, but I was unsure what to make of him. Days later he caught me online again. Was he just playing? I didn't know. We started talking about my profile with which he was extremely impressed. He said it stood out a mile and was very well written and then 'one thing led to another' ... and we came to the subject of *looks*.

'If you are fishing for a photo,' I said, 'Then you are not doing very well.'

'Not meaning to sound shallow, looks are important to me,' he replied. 'However, I have had my share of beauties and, if the personality isn't there, then there is little point. The looks thing creates the initial bond.'

Well thank the Lord for that! Was it possible that someone was on my wavelength? After a few more exchanges on the website, we began to use external email. I found his responses to be open and genuinely interested in maintaining dialogue. He seemed mature, even though he was only a year older than me. I was willing to compromise on the age thing, as this guy seemed to be worth adjusting the criteria.

'You seem more approachable this time,' he said.

The truth was that, after that night he didn't show up, I thought twice about his intentions. That scared me and so I was slightly distant.

'I don't play games,' he assured me.

He explained his situation because of which he was unable to turn up that night, and I appreciated his honesty. My respect for him grew further. He asked to move on to MSN, but the truth was that in those days I rarely used messenger and, if it came to it, then I preferred Yahoo.

'Don't worry if you don't have MSN, I will download Yahoo.'

I liked that, I really did, that he went to all that trouble for something that he would probably never use again. We moved onto Yahoo Messenger and we spoke for a while. We did engage on a mental level (he sounded as mental as I am!), but perhaps the looks issue was more important to him than he was willing to confess. He kept insisting on a photograph. I showed him one neither asking for, nor seeing, his, but he was persistent and wanted to see more. Funnily enough, he made no effort to show me his. I began to have mixed feelings about him. Maybe he didn't mean what he said about personality?

'What is your name?' he asked.

'What did I tell you last time?'

'Nasreen.'

'Well chances are that it is still *Nasreen.*'

'I think I know who this might be.'

When he said this, it made me think too. This couldn't be who I began to think it was … surely it couldn't? Life was unpredictable and the world a small place; the cyber one even smaller, but what were the chances that it could be him? No, this could not be. It just couldn't.

We had met briefly through a mutual friend from college days and no one was to know that seven years later our paths would cross as a result of an advert that I would place on the Internet in search of a partner. After this brief online encounter, we never did 'communicate' again. His emphasis on looks had been off-putting and that was a shame.

Tired of the constant games that fate would play with me, I decided to take a much needed break from the search. My strength was diminishing rapidly and so I hid my profile. Eventually, months later I decided to delete it and stop using the site altogether. Soon after, I received an invite from him to join a mobile friends' network but I didn't sign up for it. What was the point? He clearly wanted looks. Besides, if he was who I thought he might be, then we knew the same people and that felt weird.

A year or so later, a friend cried on my shoulder that she wasn't meeting any decent men. Her parents had been worried about her too, and when she told me this, as usual, I wanted to help. I fed the request into my *brain-database* thinking about who might be suitable for her.

He came to mind. She was a highly attractive young woman and that is what he sought, no matter how much he tried to shroud it. I was convinced that they would get on. But the problem was that I didn't know if he was married by now. After all, it had been a long time since we had had any contact. I searched to see if I had any known details, but no luck.

I gave up on that idea until, weeks later, by accident I found his email address scribbled on a tiny piece of paper buried in some long-forgotten documents. If this wasn't fate then I don't know what was! I wrote to him asking if he was single and if he was interested in my friend.

'I think I know who you are,' he said.

Emails bounced back and forth until he told me to call him so that we could discuss the situation. I did call, and we talked for over an hour. There was a lot to catch up on, and it was pleasant to speak with him. When I mentioned my friend he said, 'I think I already know this person, and when someone asked me recently, I said I wasn't interested.'

Surely this wasn't the same girl! He went on to admit that looks were at the top of the list and he wasn't going to speak with anyone that he wasn't attracted to. I persuaded him to at least give it a try. He said he would contact her, but days went by and he hadn't. Now, as difficult as it is to believe, women tend to be rather dumb when it comes to the *'I'll call you'* business and we actually believe that men will call us when they say that they will.

However since he hadn't, she had over those few days, maintained, or at least tried to maintain, some sort of contact. Finally he called and they spoke briefly. By that time, I came to find out that she had been exploring another avenue; I also learnt that he had become more inclined towards a spiritual life than he previously had been. If that was the case, then this girl was not suitable for him.

She even asked me, 'Why would you think that we would get on? ... He does know that I am the total opposite to you, right?'

This left me in a difficult position; what should I do? This would not work between them. I had made an error in judgement about their suitability.

I had been for a job a few weeks back, and I didn't get it. I was fairly disappointed as it seemed so right for me alas fate thought otherwise. Varsha comforted me, using her own experience of a past job opportunity as an example.

She had applied for a position but there had been a mix-up with the potential employer. As a result, they rang her that morning asking if she could come within the next hour for the interview. Just by chance the better business suits had been at the dry cleaners and she said that she was left with the one she hated. But there was no choice. She went along to the interview wearing it. Even though she was a strong candidate and had been tailor made for that role, the interviewer had judged her on appearance. Varsha said she came home disappointed that they failed to take into account that they had given her just an hour to prepare and arrive.

Varsha went on to find a role in which she thrived and flourished, rising to enormous success in such a short time, earning acclaim and respect from her superiors who realised what a unique and valuable asset she was to them. Years later, at a conference, she gave a speech and one manager was left so impressed that he approached her with a job offer. This manager was the same one who had refused to hire her previously.

Of course by now, Varsha had found something more befitting and worthy of her but this showed, she told me, that when something which could have been yours overlooks you, somehow, and for some unknown reason, you will find it back in your path at a later stage. What you do with it is then your choice. *'Disappointed I am sure ... but, if it's yours, it will come back to you,'* she told me and so, the important thing was to remember that, what has the potential to be ours will find its way to us and, if it is truly ours, then with us is where it will stay.

This got me thinking ... was fate telling me something? Had destiny finally decided that it was time? I pondered over our conversations from way back then and I remembered how much rapport we had had. That rapport was very much alive when we spoke on the phone, days earlier. Maybe it was obvious, yet I couldn't see?

Things happen for a reason. People come back to our paths for a reason. Could there be a reason why time had united us? He had come looking for me once, and said that he didn't want to lose me (we had laughed at the spelling!) and I didn't want to be lost. Now, I had gone looking for him, thinking that I was helping someone else. When deep down perhaps it was me that I wanted to help, without even realising? I wrote to him finally deciding to bite the bullet and be upfront:

> The truth of it all is that I cannot offer you status
> (and I am PMT-ish most of the time)
> (and I am also scared of change)
> (and I am never on time)
> (and I usually have dessert before the meal)
> (and I used to suffer very bad road rage, although this is now under some degree of control)
> But all I offer is to love you in the way a woman was created to love a man.

He replied saying that he did not feel the same way even though he was flattered. He prayed and hoped that I would find someone who was worthy and would return my affection but that that man was not him. He asked me to forgive him if he sounded cruel but he maintained that being honest and open from the start would ensure that no one would get hurt.

I replied back:

> Honesty is the best policy and I respect and appreciate that you were able to be upfront with me. That is why I felt the need to say what I did – I don't know how to play games and at thirty-two, am not in the

mood to start learning to either!! Besides we both
agreed that games are so passé (dahling!) !! lol

Your words are not cruel or harsh at all; each person
must do what is right for them. In life opportunities
may come to us in all sorts of shapes and it matters
not what the outcome is, but whether we were brave
enough to recognise and act upon them. I don't live a
life of regret, and so am not ashamed of anything.

With regards to my friend – I need to clear something up.
I want to assure you that there was nothing under-
handed about the whole situation. We often believe
what we want to, based on assumption, so it is
important that you understand my predicament.
I did contact you for her (through friends, have tried
to introduce her to someone suitable previously also).
However, I realised afterwards that you were perhaps
at a different place to her, and when I found out that
she was perhaps seeing another, I felt that she was
not right for you. By that time it was too late.

I debated with myself whether I should say something. And all sorts of things went through my
mind. I had promised myself that I wouldn't ever be
so upfront with anyone again, but I don't know, deep
down there was something telling me that I had to

(must start taking medication again – these voices are not good for my health!).

Everyone looks for a hand to hold through this life, and it is foolish not to explore the many chances that come our way. Yes, the pens have lifted and the pages dried, but one must not forget that this world is a world of means, sometimes destiny comes looking for you, and other times, one must go in its quest.

You will find what you seek when the time is right. A most appropriate and highly beautiful *ayah* of the Qur'an, "*He says, 'Be!' and it is.*"

Sincerest wishes,
Nasreen

Destiny had sent me another 'No'. And like a fisherman caught in stormy seas, I prayed that my boat would survive the weather and that soon my Lord would steer me to calmer waters of a welcoming shore that had been anticipating my arrival.

Twenty-five: Censored

The profiles that I have presented so far were all the ones that were approved by the website. There was one which they did not let through, however. For weeks, I protested and appealed that they allow it, but they kept refusing saying that they were unconvinced that this was a profile for the purpose of matrimony. I will let you be the judge:

The client, a thoroughbred in the diamond industry, is seeking a consummate managing partner to take her to newer and more successful heights in this acquisitions and merger bid.

THE ROLE:

Principally, the role will focus on developing and implementing a strategic life plan that supports emotional, psychological, physiological and spiritual objectives with the extended possibility of other future system requirements.

There will be a need to review and evaluate existing hard- and software in order to create and mentor a small support team. Immeasurable opportunity for upward mobility on the promotional ladder as a result of increased network of small support team.

THE PERSON:

-You are a professional first and foremost who knows diamonds.

- You will be a creative and innovative thinker who understands that success comes from building solid relationships with others and tenaciously aspiring to bring out the best in yourself in a nurturing environment that offers vast opportunity and reward for your dedication and determination.

- You will have impeccable presentation skills and will be able to adapt to varying situations accordingly, efficiently and effectively.

- Excellent written skills are imperative as you will be required to communicate on a deeper level with the client and reach an unsurpassable mental connection with her.

- Ability to persuade senior management to implement system changes is also essential.

- Experience in handling sensitive goods is desired, and passion would be highly regarded, as would great attention to detail.

- Reasonable proficiency in honesty, integrity and manners are expected and quality should come as standard. Training will not be given.

- Furthermore, ambition, spirit, motivation, enthusiasm, stamina and patience will greatly enhance your chances.

If you want a rewarding future full of opportunity and challenge within a diverse, dynamic and exciting environment, then our client can offer unlimited potential for your professional and personal development.

This outstanding opportunity will suit a practical results driven achiever who seeks an attractive remuneration package. (Prevaricators ought to be aware that this role will prove difficult for them to master.)

Regrettably, this is a permanent role, and those looking for temporary contracts or other freelance opportunities need not respond. Please also note that the selection process will entail a fair amount of rigorous psychometric testing; therefore the ability to tie your horse upon arrival is essential.

[Remember, it should never be just about the sparkle, but rather about how well it cuts glass.]

They may have disallowed this profile but somehow, the man for whom I had written it must have read it, without it ever finding its way to him ... Fate decided to intervene slightly and took me to one website, where I would find a master of the web.

Twenty-six:
Whispers in My Heart – or *Just an Illusion?*

S earching for that elusive someone is an excruciatingly difficult process. Sometimes you stop. Sometimes you start again. Sometimes you give up entirely and swear that you won't ever return to it. There are also times when, as if you have no dignity, you are back; hoping … wishing … turning over every stone just in case s/he is hiding there.

Then there comes a point when you know that it's just not going to work for you. In the way that I had known that my family introducing me to eligible bachelors would not work for me, I soon came to realise that after five years of searching independently, the online matrimonial route was also not going to work for me. I surrendered and started getting used to the idea of being and dying alone. My ever optimistic and true hearted best friend, however, continued carrying that torch of hope:

'I can say fully assured that you will make someone a happy man someday, could be next week, could be next year. i can't tell you that, all I know is that you will find your prince…'

Love Varsha'

As much as I appreciated her sincerity and prayers, I had become disheartened. It wasn't to say that the Internet route didn't work for people, because I had known a few couples who had found each other through this method, it's just that no matter how hard I tried, it just wouldn't be a success for me. This, I finally accepted.

The problem now was that sitting in front of my laptop for hours on end; scouring profiles, hoping that I would find those words *'Looking for me?'* had become habitual. Having drained a considerable chunk of my life so far, online, chatting to suitors, mailing them, trying to bribe them into marrying me, now, suddenly, I was cut off from what I had come to know. This left a mammoth hole and I needed something to fill it.

By that time, I was frequenting a work-related website and there, by chance, I discovered an external link. This website had nothing to do with matrimony and I liked the fact that this word was nowhere to be found. I signed up, scepticism aside, wanting to explore this corner of cyberspace that I had stumbled upon accidentally.

The site was a lively one. There was even a forum but it was not an attraction to me. I just wanted to feed what had by now become my online addiction, so I paid up for a month, to test it out.

Just before the trial was over I had the opportunity to renew but I didn't as I had only intended to stay for a little while and didn't want to make this a permanent feature in my life. But days went by and I missed it … so I went back and renewed for another month. When that month was over I renewed again. By now, the site had grown on me so much that after that month ended, I then signed up for one year's *Supreme Membership*.

And then one day ...

Twenty-seven: Prince Charming

... ?

Epilogue

B efore we part, let us share a few thoughts. There seems to be endless debate and discussion about what women want and what men want. Shelves are overflowing with books written on this subject and Hollywood is overflowing with romantic comedies.

I think it's simple. Men want exactly what we want: love. And they seek exactly what we seek: *'The One'*. The only difference is that we make no conscious effort to control our 'desperately seeking love' antics, whereas our male counter-parts are connoisseurs at hiding this. Don't be fooled though; we both share the same underlying desire and primitive human need of loving and being loved.

Even if you think that the internet is a complete waste of time, when it comes to trying to find someone with whom to spend the rest of your life; know that somewhere in this world, your *yet-to-be spouse* is thinking the exact same thing. It is only a matter of time before you find each other and when fate is ready, you will know.

Patience, gratitude and good intentions are words that perhaps mean near to nothing for despondent readers out there, but these are in fact the essential ingredients to the search and life in general. Just remember that everything happens for a reason and that at the time it may be difficult to comprehend, however, when it is meant, it will be said, *'Be!'* and so it shall ... This is something that we must always believe in our hearts; no matter what happens.

I wish you all peace and love (… and many babies).

Acknowledgements

Nothing in life is ever possible without a little helping hand.

Words can never express the gratitude that I have for Paul, who taught me to discover a *'me'* that I was too afraid to know. Thank you for listening.

My family, who in their own way have supported me throughout these years. I know that I neither appreciated nor valued what a blessing you all are but deep down somewhere and with the passage of time, as I get older, I realise that where you lacked in certain areas, with the things I wanted, you more than compensated in those areas with the things that I needed and could not do without but foolishly thought that I could. In particular to my brother for all the I.T. support that he provided without me ever asking and of course for putting up with my constant mood swings.

I am indebted to the Prince's Trust who took a chance to make this dream possible. Julie Macken, who invested all that faith in me and Debra Winterson, my superwoman friend who then helped lift that faith. Thank you for finding this book interesting!

Leon Hines, the jewel in any legal crown. Thank you for everything that you have done for me out of the kindness of your heart. Your professionalism and expertise are the finest.

Yasmin Alibhai-Brown, who welcomed me into her home and her life with a love so gentle as if she had known me for years (… and for not giving away those crystal flowers!).

Rakesh Patel for wanting to have his name appear in someone's book. (//Didn't matter whose, didn't matter how, just that it did.)

Varsha who not only went above and beyond her duties as a friend to me, but is also the first person to ever buy this book when eventually it was made available to the world – You're so *extra!!* … xx

For precious friends: Bobby, my sister with a beautiful heart. Rehana, who refused to give up on me … *'I love what you've done with your window!'* W: *FFS*. Sin, whose top-grade humour is just beyond description, *'Mav, you can be my wingman any time.'*

For tab, one very special person who has taught me that in this world there are genuine selfless people who honour the true meaning of friendship . . . *'O kee kehndey neh …'*

And of course that great Prince fan, a great Prince himself whose presence, albeit from a distance, has made this journey that little bit sweeter.

Finally, to all who have read this book, I hope that you have enjoyed it. Said William Wordsworth, *'Fill your paper with the breathings of your heart,'* and that is exactly what I have tried to do here. Please forgive me for my shortcomings, they are entirely my own.

Glossary

Allah	The Arabic word for God; the same monotheistic God of Abraham whose progeny from one son, Isaac, gave way to Judaism and the progeny of the other son, Ishmail (be upon them all peace), brought the seal of the Message with Islam
Allah Hafiz (Al-Hafiz)	God is the Protector
Allah Malik (Al-Malik)	God is the King
Al-Adl	The Just
Al-Aleem	The All-Knowing
Al Hakeem	The All-Wise
Ar-Rahman	The Most Gracious
Ar-Raheem	The Especially Merciful
As-Salaam	The Forebearer of Peace
Alayis Salaam	Muslims are required to invoke God's blessings and peace upon the Prophets whenever their name is mentioned, e.g. Musa (*alayis Salaam*) = Moses, be upon him peace; Blessed Virgin Maryam (*alayis Salaam*) = Mary, be upon her peace; Isa (*alayis Salaam*) = Jesus Christ, be upon him peace
Ameen	A supplication meaning; 'O God, please accept our invocation'
Al hamdu lillah	'All thanks be to God'
Ayah	Verse of the Qur'an; also means a sign
Azza wa jall	Glorified and Sublime be He
Bhelpuri	Indian appetiser
Dua	Supplication
Eeman/Eiman	Faith
Fajr	Dawn prayer
Ghayb	Unseen/Unknown
Halal	Permissible under Islam

Hijab	Commonly used to refer to the headscarf worn by Muslim women but it literally means 'to cover'. It is the body's self-covering for dignity and modesty and relates to a whole system of attitude and behaviour. Thus I prefer the phrase 'observe *hijab*' as opposed to 'wear *hijab*'
Hadith	Recorded sayings or traditions of Prophet Muhammad (*salallahu alayhi wa sallum*)
Hikmah	Wisdom
Haraam	Forbidden; opposite to halal
Iddah	The time of waiting prescribed for women who get divorced or widowed which they must spend before entering into another marriage, if they want to
Imam	The one who leads the congregational prayer
In sha Allah	God willing
Islam	Submission to God; root of the word means 'Peace, submission, obedience and purity'
Jilbab	Long, baggy outer garment worn by some Muslim women
Jannah	Paradise
Ji	Term which denotes a mark of respect, usually said after a person's name
Jihad	Struggle; earnest personal or physical striving in the way of God for righteousness and against acts of wrongdoing
Jihad Akbar	'Greater Jihad': Internal struggle of the lower desires of the soul against evil and temptation such as lust, greed, envy etc. which serve to corrupt the Muslim taking him/her away from the remembrance and obedience of Allah
Jihad Asghar	'Lesser Jihad': Defence, fighting to protect Islam from attack or oppression. In such defence, no woman, child or civilian is to be harmed and neither is a tree to be cut down
Laddu	Yellow ball shaped traditional South Asian sweets distributed upon hearing good news
Layla-tul Qadr	A Blessed Night found during the last ten days

	of *Ramadhan*, the Muslim month of fasting
Lehnga	Bridal dress
Maghrib	Sunset prayer
Ma sha Allah	God has willed it
Masjid	Mosque
Muhammad	The Seal of the Prophets of Allah; the Last and Final Messenger who reiterated the message brought mankind by Adam, Noah, Abraham, Jacob, Isaac, Moses, Joseph, David, Solomon and the Son of the Blessed Virgin Mary: Jesus Christ (may the Peace and Blessings of the Almighty God, the Most Glorious, the Supremely Majestic be upon them all of His Prophets)
Mullahs	Religious leaders, theologians
Muslim	Follower of the Islamic faith; one who submits their will to God
Nafs	Lower desires of the soul
Niqaab	Face veil worn by some Muslim women
Pahari	Spoken variety of language of people originating from Mirpur, Pakistan
Ramadhan	The Muslim month of fasting
Qur'an	The literal word of God and culmination of God's revelation to mankind, revealed to Prophet Muhammad in the year AD 610
Rishta	Candidate for marriage or marriage proposal
Rishtey	Plural of *Rishta*
Salaam	See entry for *As-Salaam*
Sallalahu alaihi wa sallam	'May the peace and blessings of Allah be upon him.' Muslims say this whenever the name of the Prophet Muhammad appears or is heard
Shareef	Decent
Shalwar	Traditional Pakistani trousers
Shalwar kameez	Traditional Pakistani clothing consisting of a top and bottoms
Shaytaan	Arabic word for Satan; also *Iblis*
Subhan'Allah	Term used to express joy. Means 'All Praises are for God'

Sunnah	Ways of the Prophet Muhammad, his habits, teachings and lifestyle
Surah	Chapter of the Qur'an
Tahajjud	Last third of the night, just before the *Fajr* (dawn) prayer
Yaum-ul Qiyama	Day of Judgement
Wali	Protector; guardian
Wa-alaikum as-Salaam	Reply to the Islamic greeting '*As-Salaamun Alaikum*' (Peace be with you). The reply means 'Peace be with you as well'
Wa'Allahi	I swear by Allah's Blessed Name
Wudhu	Ablution in preparation for prayer

Endnotes

(i)   Narration by Dawud Wharnsby Ali in *'Timeless Wisdom'*, the Holy
        Qur'an presented in melodic tone with English translation. Clas-
        sical Arabic recited by Abdul Basit Abdul Samad, and English
        translation read by Dawud Wharnsby Ali.© 2001 Soundvi-
        sion.com

(ii)   *Sahih Muslim* Book 42 Number 7058
        This is Hadith 40, from the *An-Nawawis Forty Hadith*, generally
        regarded as the most popular anthology of Prophetic sayings.
        http://fortyhadith.iiu.edu.my/hadith40.htm

(iii)   Abu Darda, may Allah be pleased with him, said "I heard the
        Messenger of Allah (be upon him peace) say:

*'For him who seeks a road to knowledge, Allah eases a road to Paradise. The
angels lower their wings to him who seek knowledge, in satisfaction with what
he is doing. All those in the Heavens and those on earth, even the fish in the
water, seek forgiveness for the knowledgeable. In Allah's eyes, a knowledgeable
person is superior to an ordinary worshipper as the moon is superior in
brilliance to the other heavenly bodies. The ulema [people of knowledge] are the
heirs of the Prophets. The Prophets did not bequeath a dirham or a dinar.
They only left knowledge; and that is a great fortune for those who grasp it.'*

[Related by Abu Da'ud, at Tirmidhi, ibn Majah, Ibn Hibban and
al-Bayhaqi]. Quoted on page 9, Salih Ajjaj, M. M. (1993) *Jewels of
Guidance*, Dar al-Taqwa, ISBN 1 870582 00 4

(iv)   http://www.usc.edu/dept/MSA/fundamentals/hadithsunnah
        /scienceofhadith/aape.html Appendix 6

(v)   Islamic Foundation, ISBN 0-86037-292-8; Al-Qaradaawee, Y.
        (2000) *Time in the Life of a Muslim*, Ta-Ha Publishers Ltd, ISBN 1-
        84200-007-1; Ibn Qayyim al-Jawziyyah (2003) *Provisions for the
        Hereafter*, Darussalam, ISBN 9960-897-18-4; Ibn Qayyim al-

Jawziyyah (trans. Nasiruddin al-Khattab) (1997) *Patience and Gratitude*, Ta-Ha Publishers Ltd, ISBN 1 897940 610; Al-Khater, A. (trans. Al-Arabee, A. H.) (2001) *Grief and Depression*, ISBN 1-874263-76-0; Abdullah, R (1999) *Trials and Tribulations*, Ta-Ha Publishers Ltd, ISBN 1 897940 890; Roushdy, Y. (1999) *Allah: the Divine Nature*, Dar al Taqwa Ltd. ISBN 1-870582-31-4; 'Aaidh ibn Abdullah al-Qarnee (2002) *Don't Be Sad*, International Islamic Publishing House, ISBN 9960-672-77-8

(vi)   *Hadith Qudsi 15. Hadith Qudsi are the sayings of the Prophet Muhammad* (be upon him peace) as revealed to him by the Almighty Allah. *Hadith Qudsi* [or Sacred Hadith] are so named because, unlike the majority of Hadith which are Prophetic Hadith, their *sanad* [authority] is traced back not to the Prophet but to the Almighty. Among the many definitions given by the early scholars to Sacred Hadith is that of as-Sayyid ash-Sharif al-Jurjani (died in 816 AH) in his lexicon At-Tarifat where he says: 'A Sacred Hadith is, as to the meaning, from Allah the Almighty; as to the wording, it is from the messenger of Allah (PBUH). It is that which Allah the Almighty has communicated to His Prophet through revelation or in dream, and he, peace be upon him, has communicated it in his own words. Thus Qur'an is superior to it because, besides being revealed, it is His wording.'
http://www.usc.edu/dept/MSA/fundamentals/hadithsunnah/hadithqudsi.html

(vii)   Extract from an article entitled 'A Wife'
http://www.alinaam.org.za/library/marital/awife.htm As stated on the article this is a talk by Shaykh Abdullah Adhami. No part of the extract used has been edited in any way and is as was found on the website on Monday 23rd March 2007. In accordance to the copyright disclaimer featured at the bottom of the article, ali-naam@alinaa.org.za was notified about the author's intention to use the extract of 39 words.

(viii)   *'Inna anzalnahu fee laylatialqadri*
Wama adraka ma laylatualqadri
Laylatu alqadri khayrun min alfi shahrin
Tanazzalu almala-ikatu waalrroohufeeha bi-ithni rabbihim min kulli amrin
Salamun hiya hatta matlaAAialfajri'

'We have indeed revealed this (Message) in the Night of Power:
And what will explain to thee what the Night of Power is?
The Night of Power is better than a thousand months
Therein come down the angels and the Spirit by Allah's permission, on every errand
Peace! ...... This until the rise of morn!'

(*Surah Al Qadr*, Power, Fate 97: 1–5)

Extract used in Chapter Fifteen, Nice – Biscuits, Guys and Girls is from an article entitled: 'The Powerless and the Night of Power' which on Monday 26th March 2007 was found on http://www.islamicity.com/articles/Articles.asp?ref=IC0112-382 [10/21/2006 – Religious – Article Ref: IC0112-382]. The extract has been used in good faith under the 'fair dealing' clause in accordance of the guidelines issued by UK-based Society of Authors and the Publishers Association. Similar to the Islamicity website's use of this article under the 'fair use' clause as recognised by US law, the author has used this extract in the present work to give greater understanding of the issue to which it relates. The copyright holder of the extract, Sadullah Khan, Director of Islamic Center of Irvine, was contacted and these intentions were communicated.

(ix)   http://www.usc.edu/dept/MSA/law/fiqhussunnah/fus3_53.h
tml